Dot-to-Dot
THERAPY

D0262713

Dot-to-Dot
THERAPY

DAVID WOODROFFE

ARCTURUS

NOTES:

Page 7   This picture is made from 3 continuous lines: a) 1 - 83, b) a - i and c) A - N

Page 18   This picture is made from 2 continuous lines: a) 1 - 344 and 2) a - n

Page 27   This picture is made from 3 continuous lines: a) 1 - 365, b) a - q and 3) A - R

Page 28   This picture is made from 4 continuous lines: a) 1 - 315, b) a - m, c) A - L and d) I - VII

Page 41   This picture is made from 2 continuous lines: a) 1 - 367 and 2) a - g

Page 43   This picture is made from 3 continuous lines: a) 1 - 394, b) a - r, and c) A - N

Page 44   This picture is made from 4 continuous lines: a) 1 - 354, b) a - N, 3) A - N and 4) I to X

Page 56   This picture is made from 2 continuous lines: a) 1 - 373 and 2) a - r

Page 58   This picture is made from 4 continuous lines: a) 1 - 355 and 2) a - p

Page 59   This picture is made from 2 continuous lines: a) 1 - 393 and 2) a - e

Page 60   This picture is made from 3 continuous lines: a) 1 - 392, b) a - j and 3) A - J

Page 63   This picture is made from 4 continuous lines: a) 1 - 352, b) a - r, 3) A - V and 4) I to IX

Page 64   This picture is made from 2 continuous lines: a) 1 - 389 and b) a - r

Page 65   This picture is made from 2 continuous lines: a) 1 - 371 and 2) a - i

Page 68   This picture is made from 4 continuous lines: a) 1 - 360 and 2) a - p

Page 73   This picture is made from 4 continuous lines: a) 1 - 360 and 2) a - i

Page 106   This picture is made from 2 continuous lines: a) 1 - 350 and 2) a - i

Page 108   This picture is made from 4 continuous lines: a) 1 - 360, b) a - Q, c) A - H and d) I - XII

Page 124   This picture is made from 2 continuous lines: a) 1 - 380 and b) a - z

ARCTURUS

This edition published in 2016 by Arcturus Publishing Limited
26/27 Bickels Yard, 151–153 Bermondsey Street,
London SE1 3HA

Copyright © Arcturus Holdings Limited

All rights reserved. No part of this publication may be reproduced,
stored in a retrieval system, or transmitted, in any form or by any means,
electronic, mechanical, photocopying, recording or otherwise, without
prior written permission in accordance with the provisions of the
Copyright Act 1956 (as amended). Any person or persons who do any
unauthorised act in relation to this publication may be liable to criminal
prosecution and civil claims for damages.

ISBN: 978-1-78404-973-7
CH004809NT
Supplier 34, Date 0416, Print Run 5322

Printed in the Czech Republic
Created for children 10+

CONTENTS

INTRODUCTION

Sudoku and crossword puzzles are often used as a means of relaxing the mind and calming down after a busy day, but in this book we offer a way of therapeutically massaging the brain without reasoning or knowledge. Instead, you just need the ability to join consecutively numbered dots using only a sharp eye and a pencil.

This can be trickier than it seems because the numbers may be in sequence but not necessarily next to each other on the page – some careful searching will often be required. But the reward will be well worth your patience as you gradually reveal an array of pictures on various themes calculated to induce pleasant thoughts and make you feel better about the world.

So sharpen your pencil and gently warm to your task by tackling the small picture opposite to see how it works.

Happy dotting!

David Woodroffe

NB: Some images are made up of more than one continuous line. For a list of these, please go to Notes on page 4.

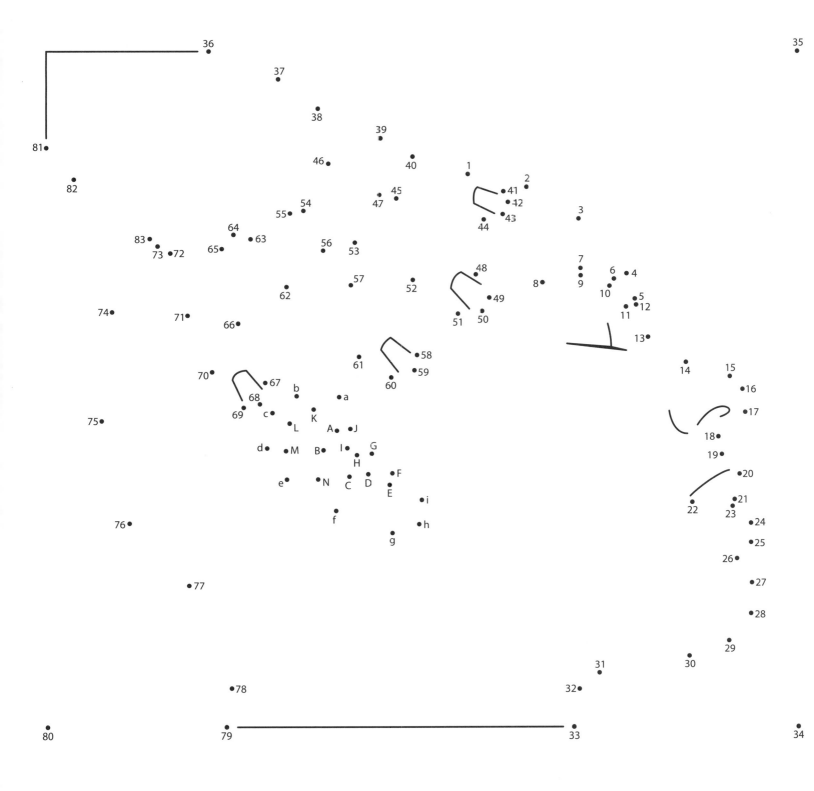

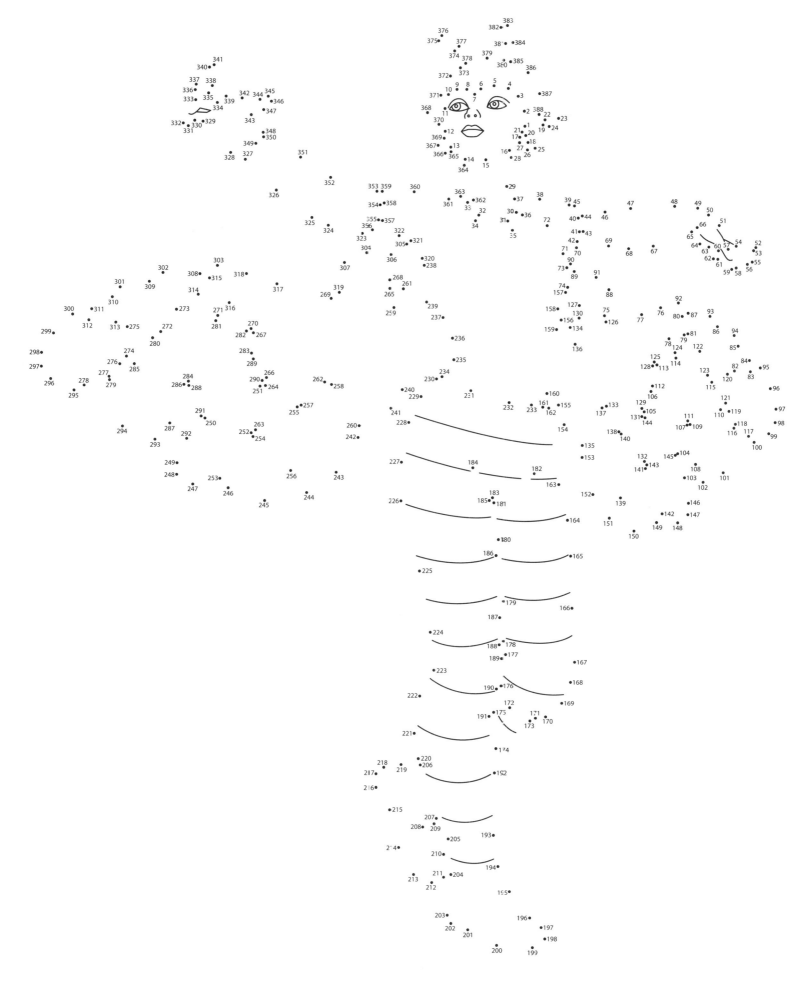

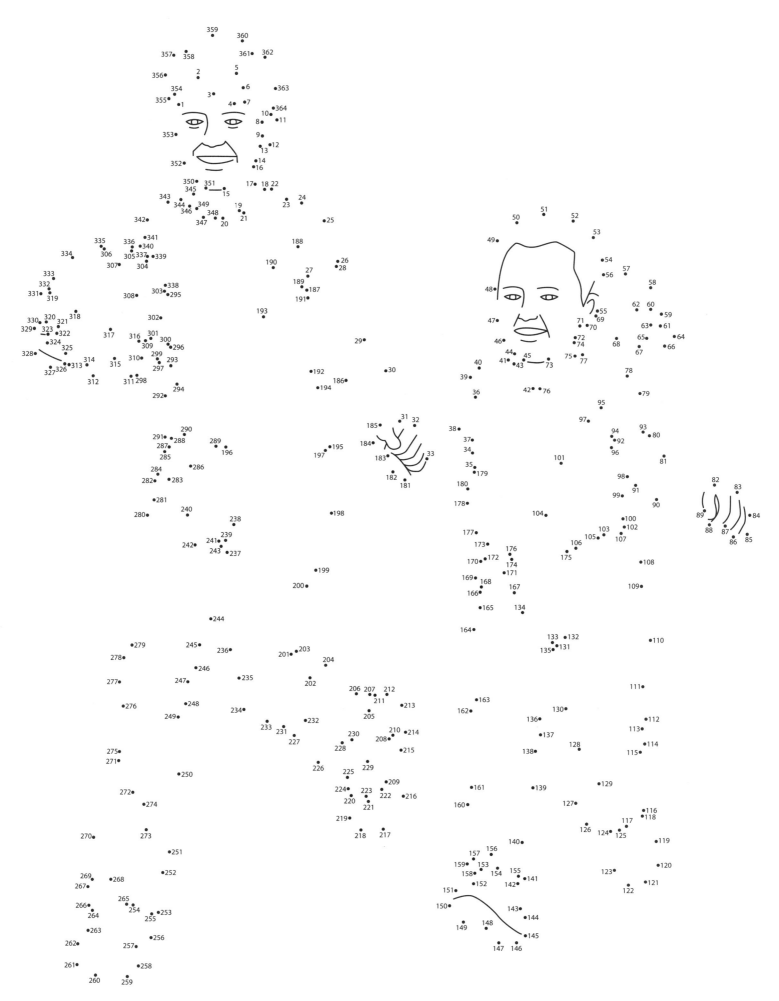

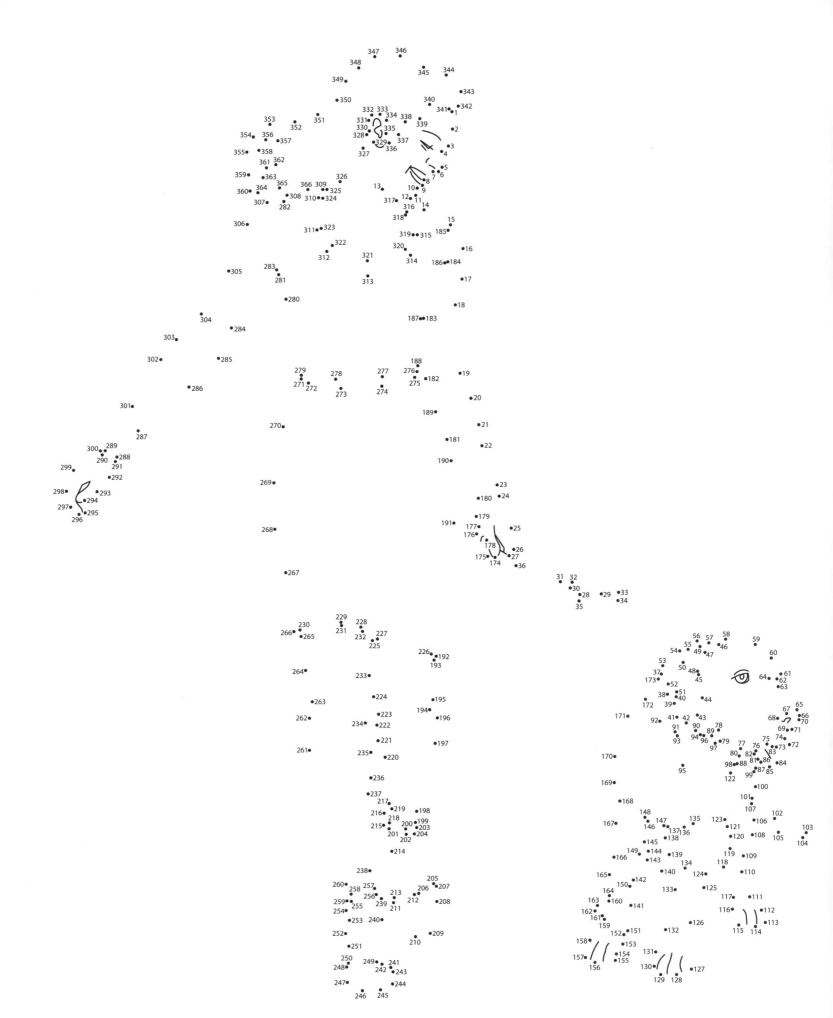

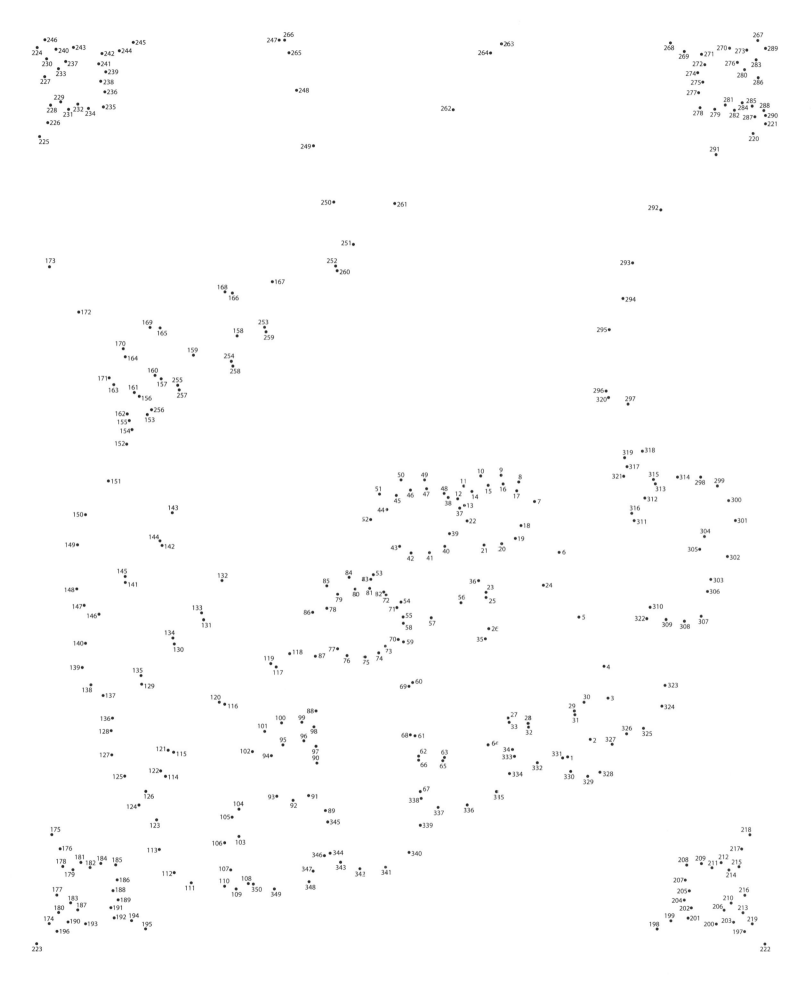

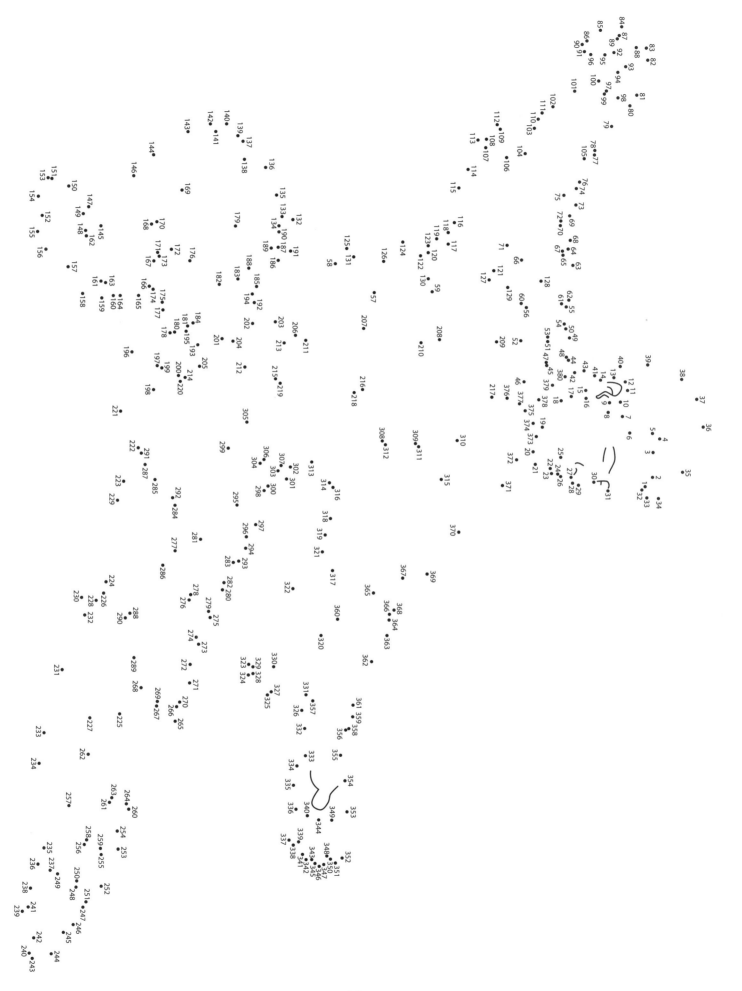

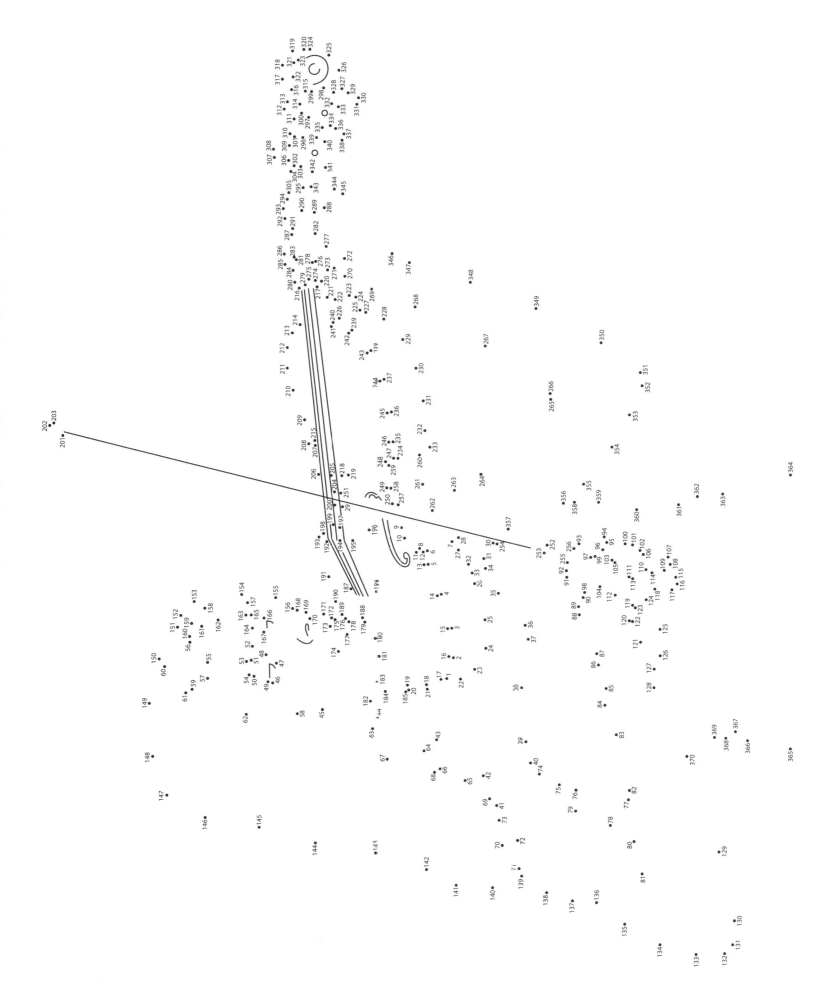

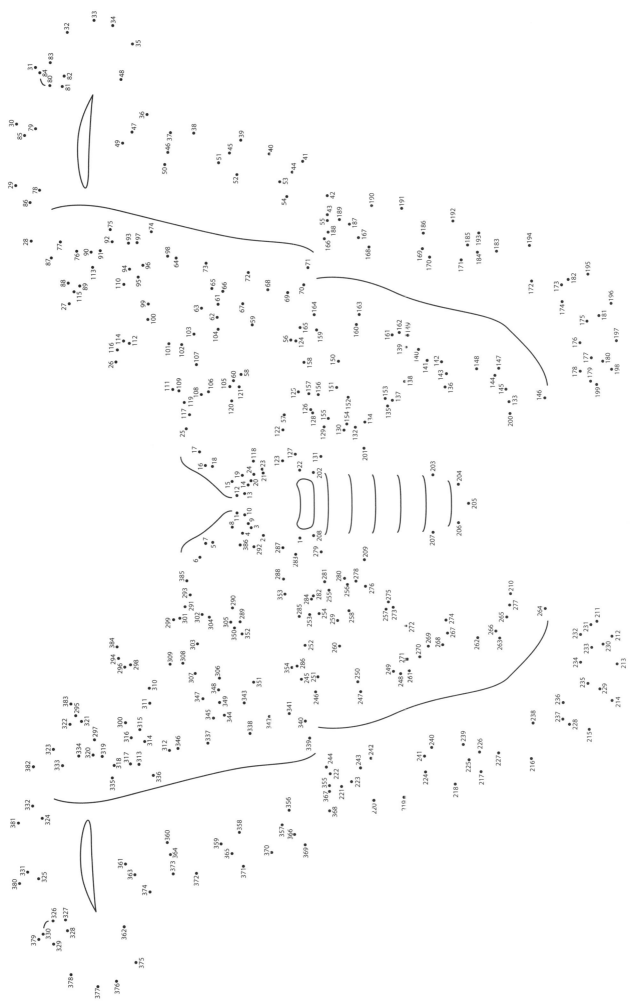

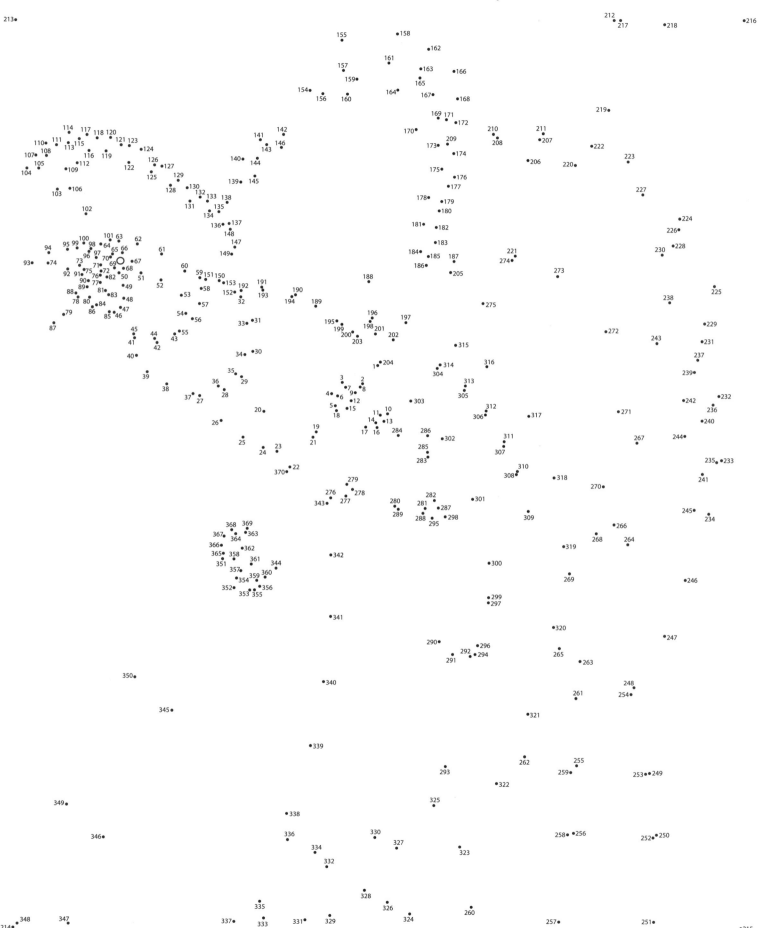

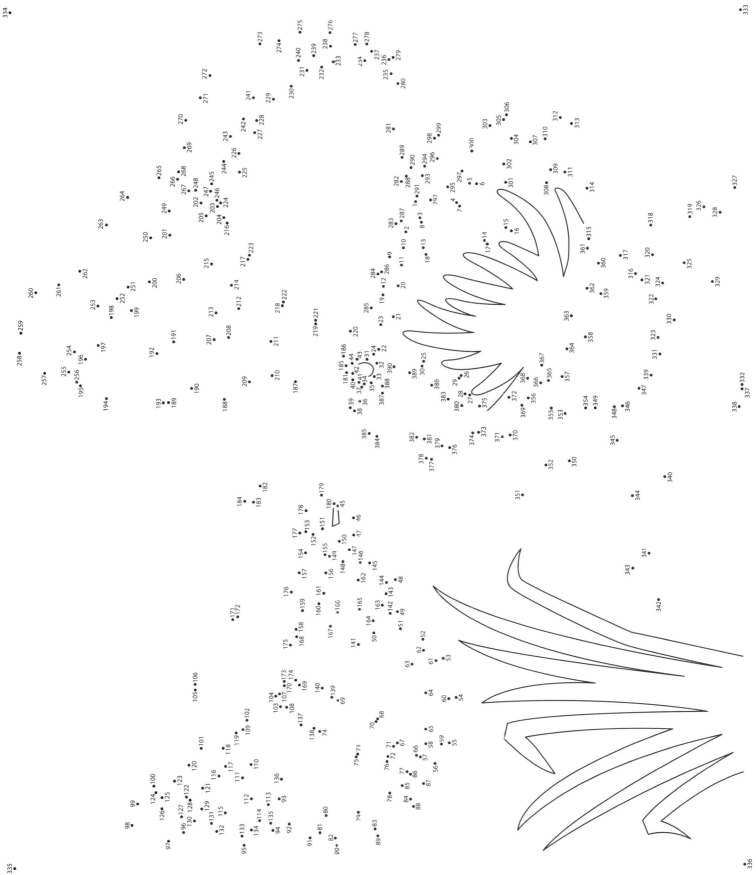

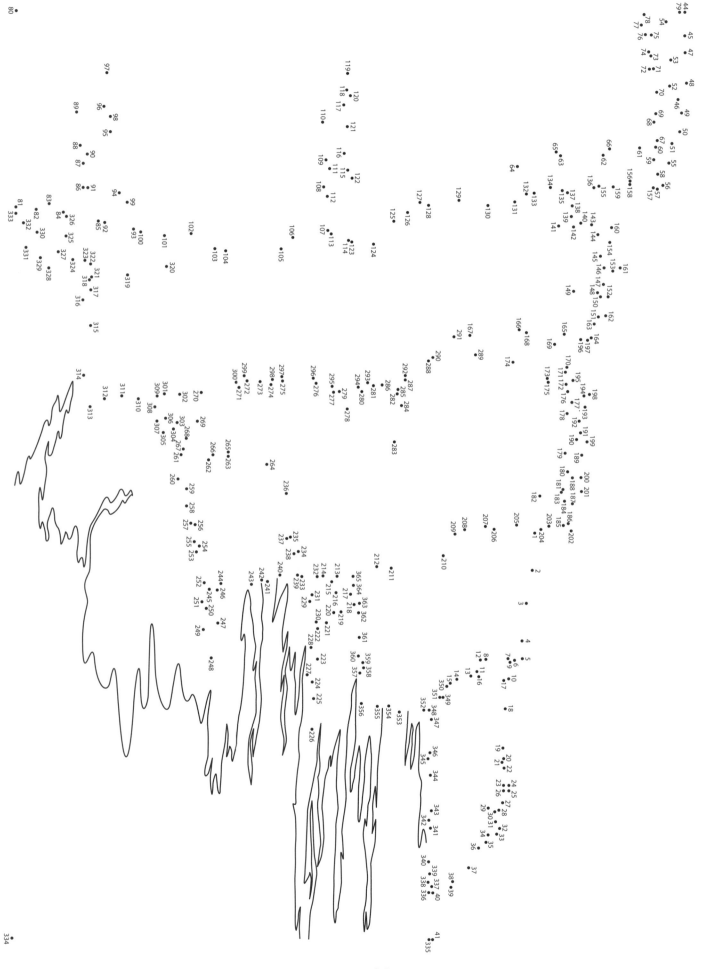

24

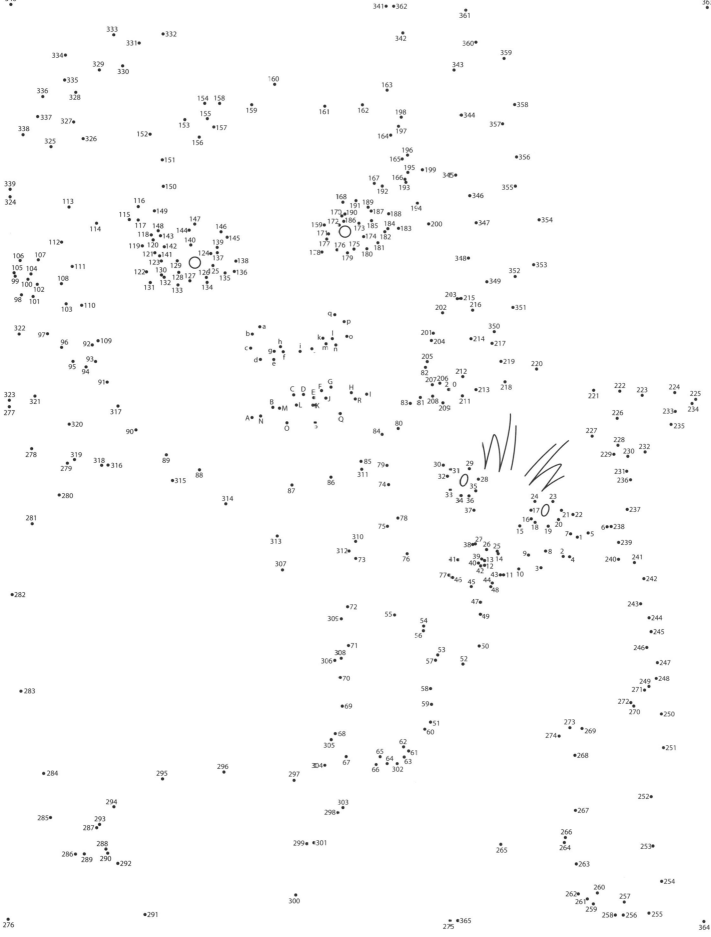

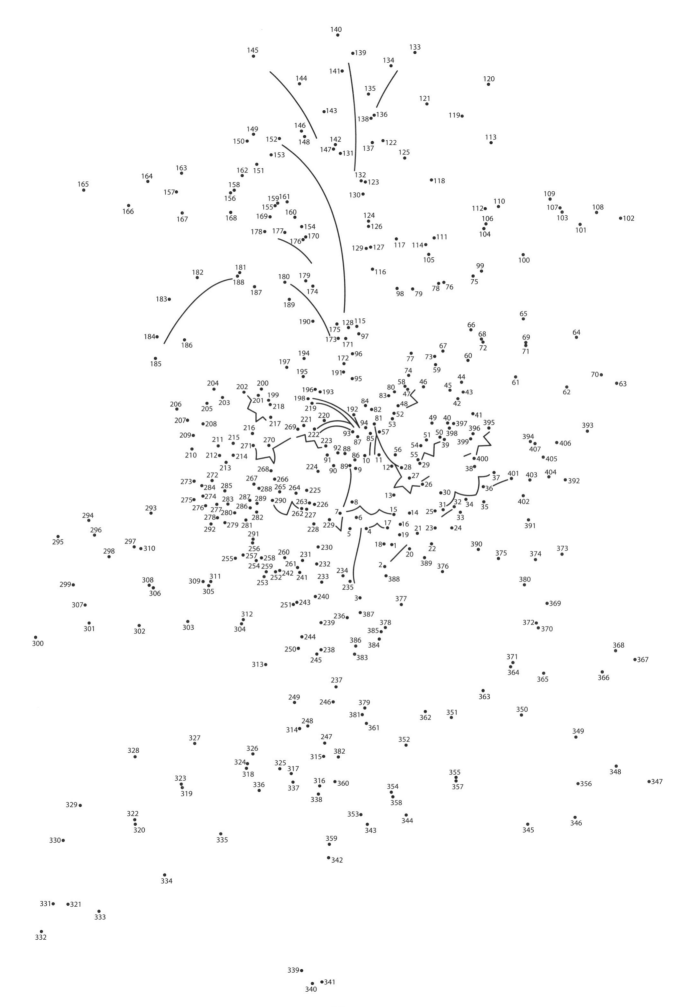

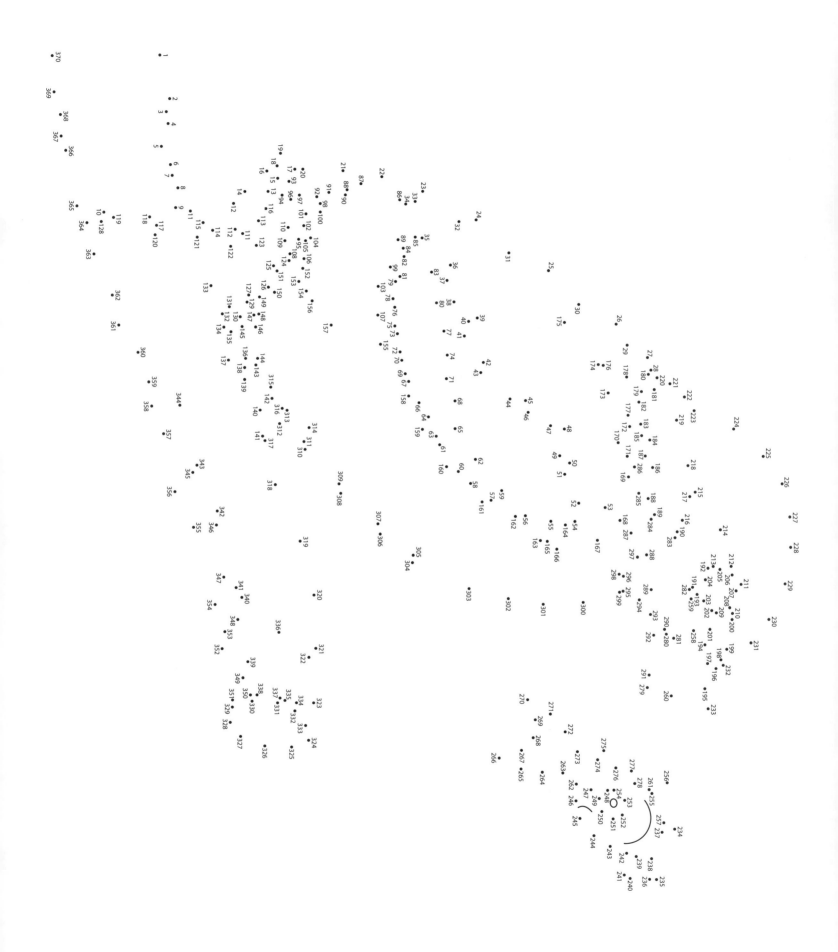

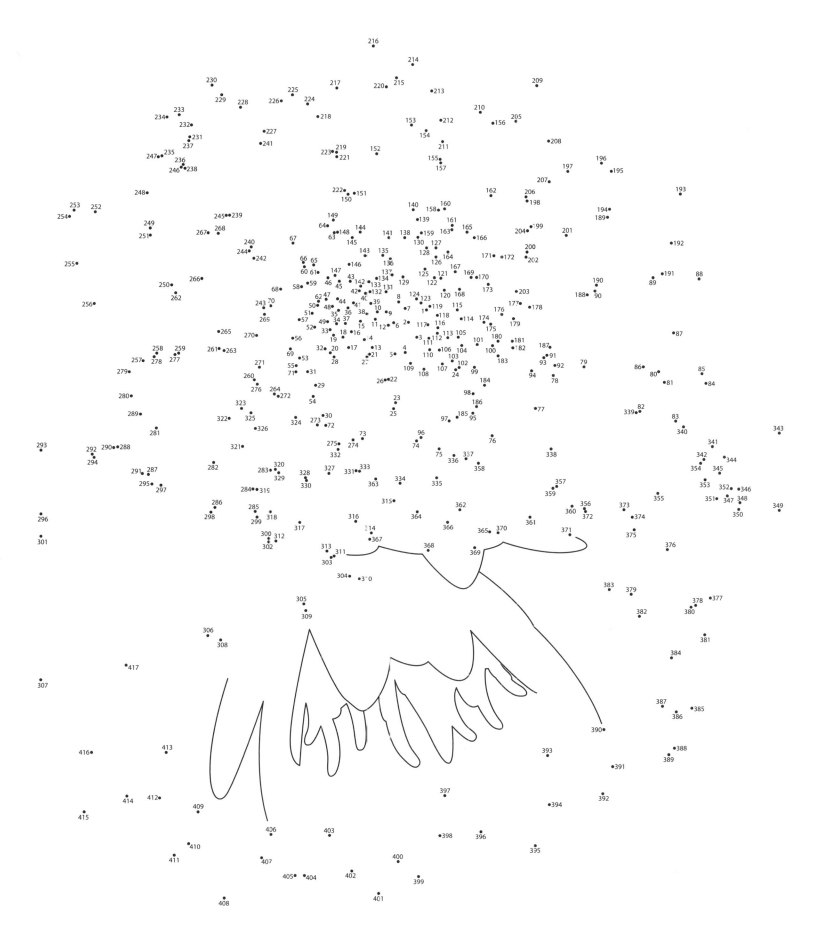

33

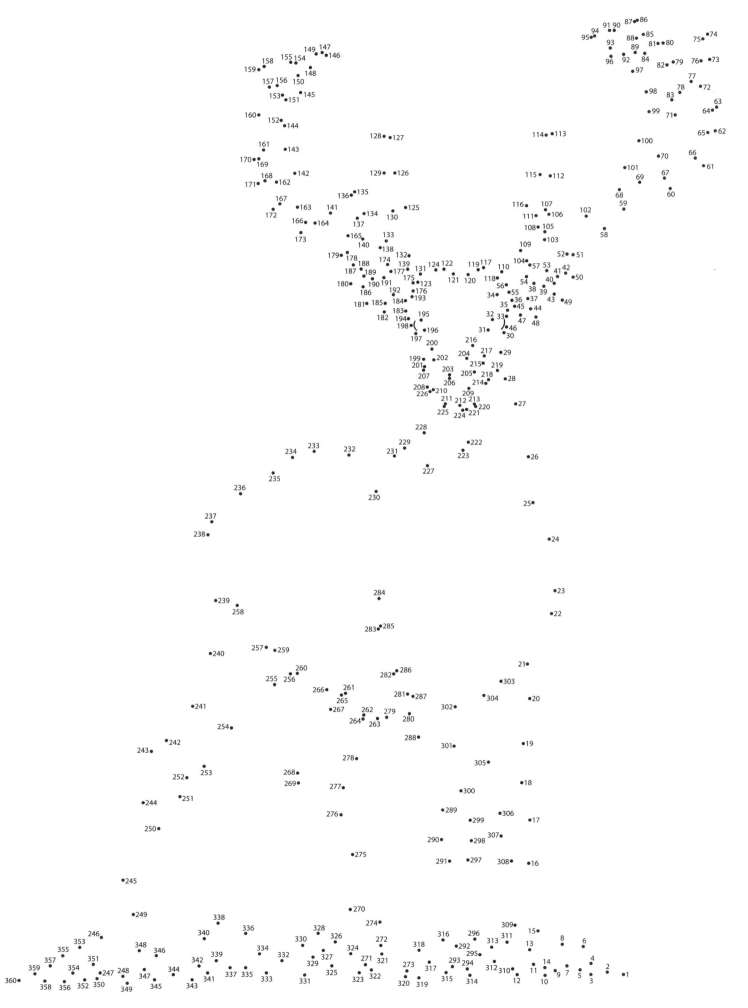

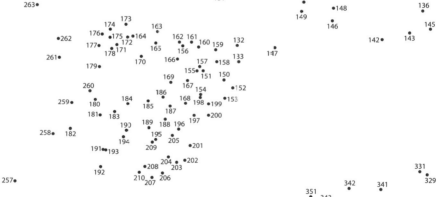

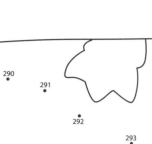

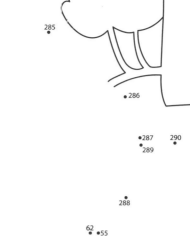

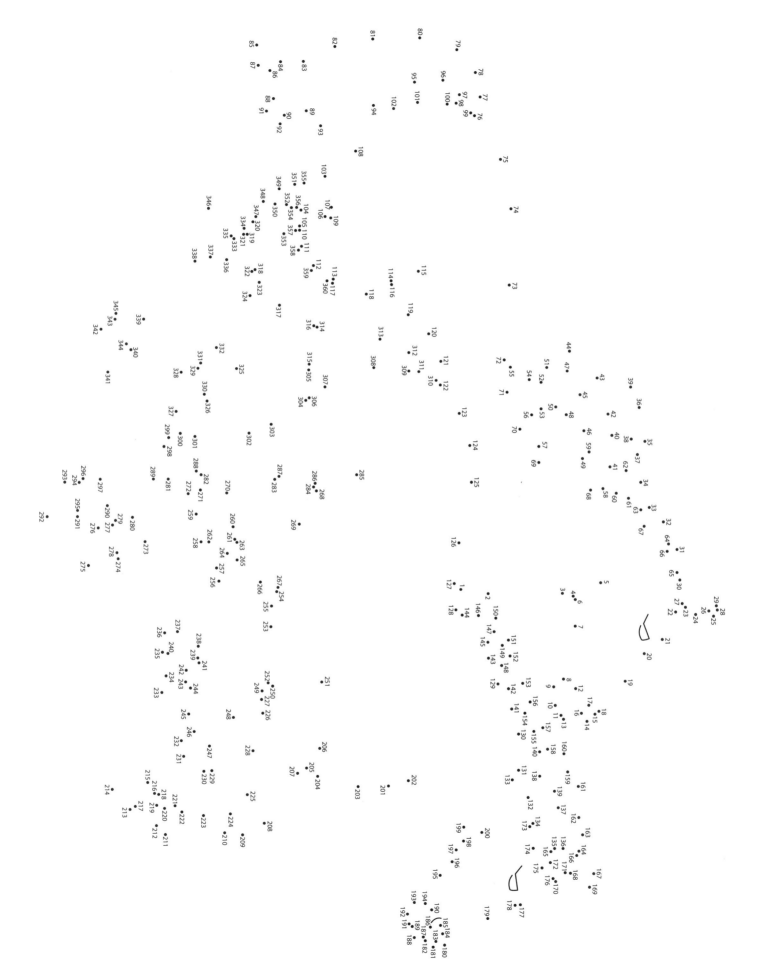

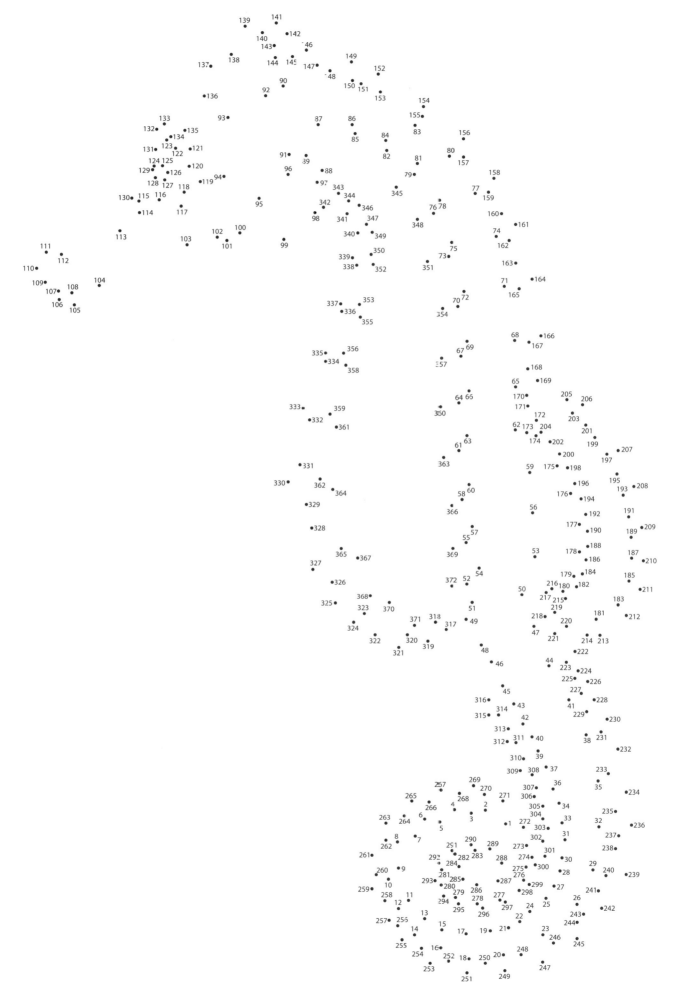

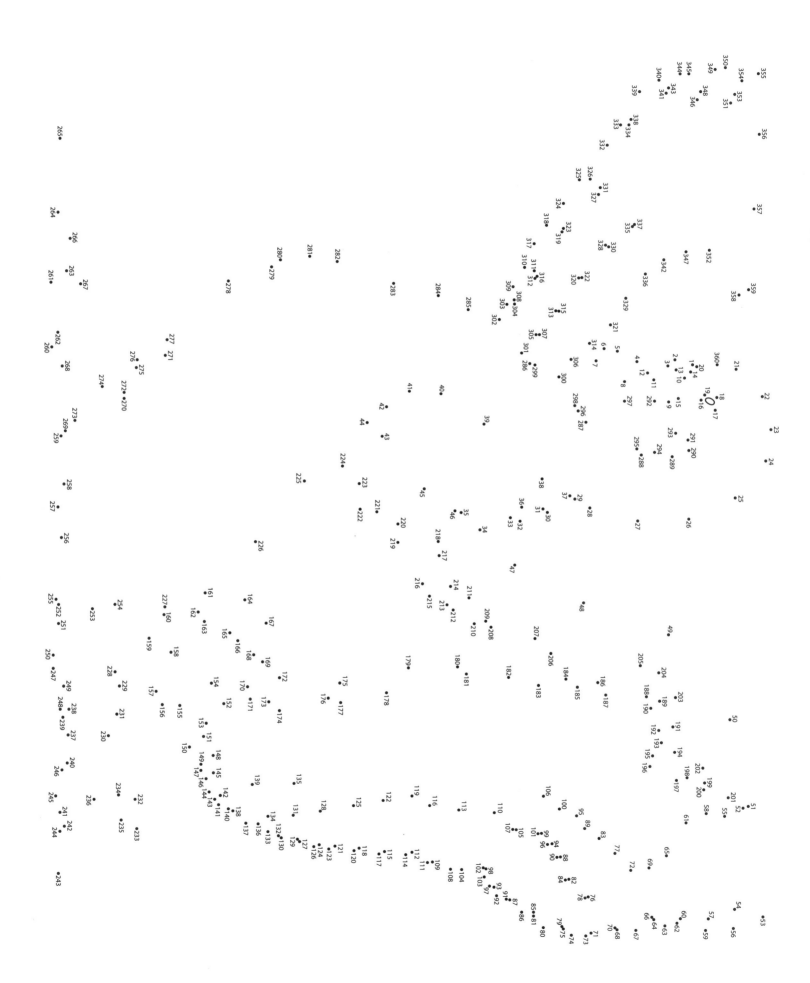

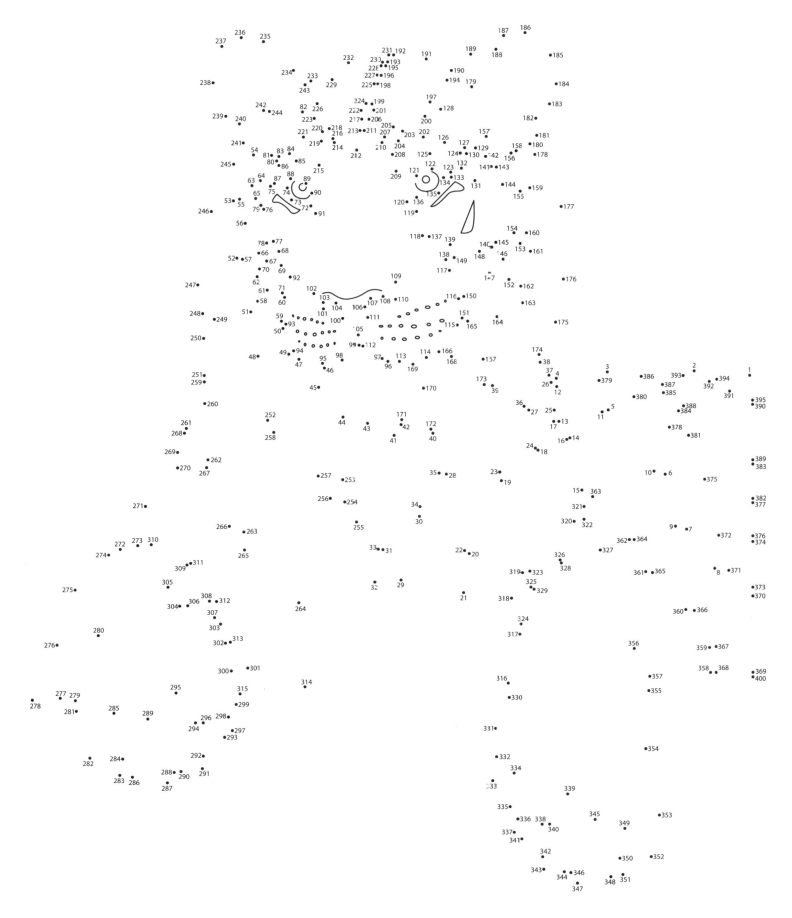

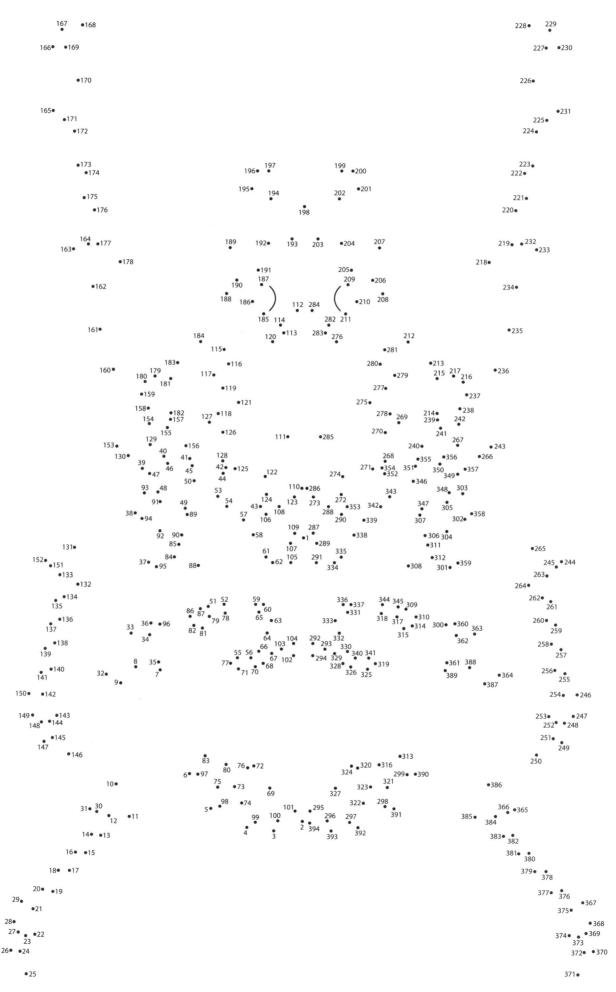

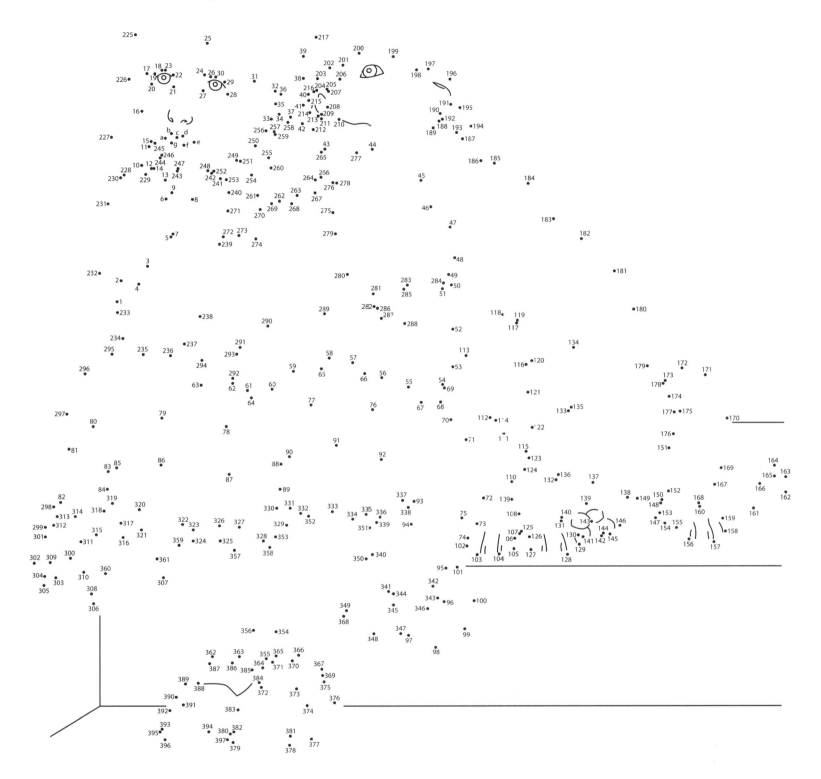

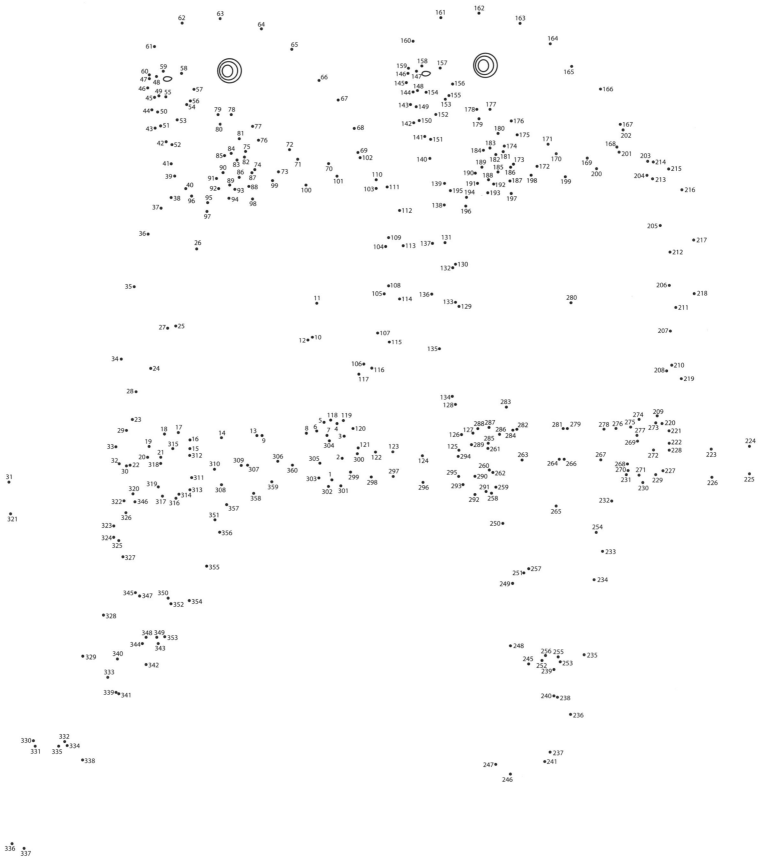

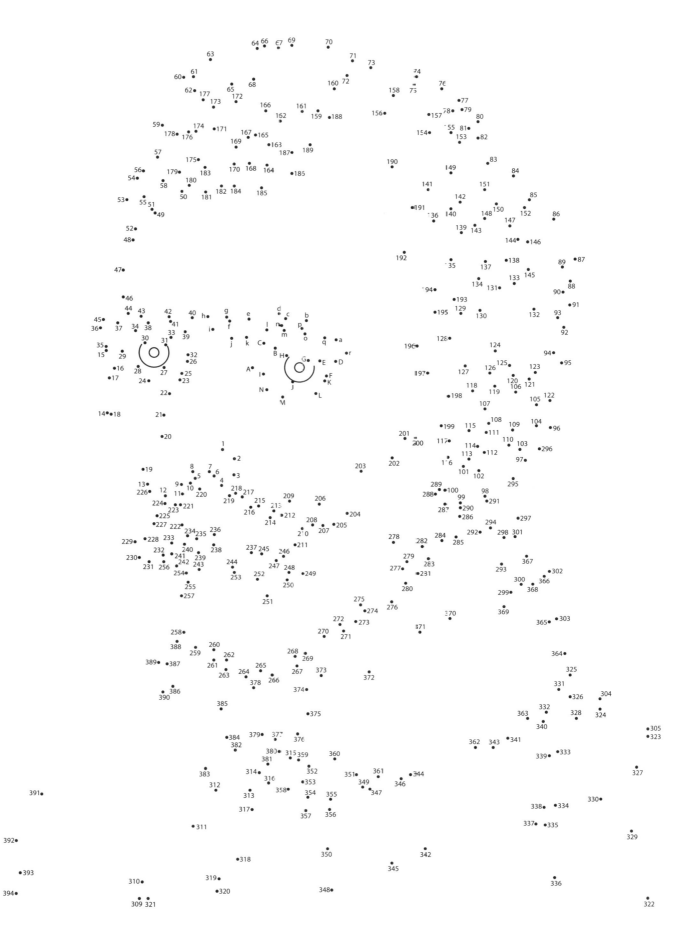

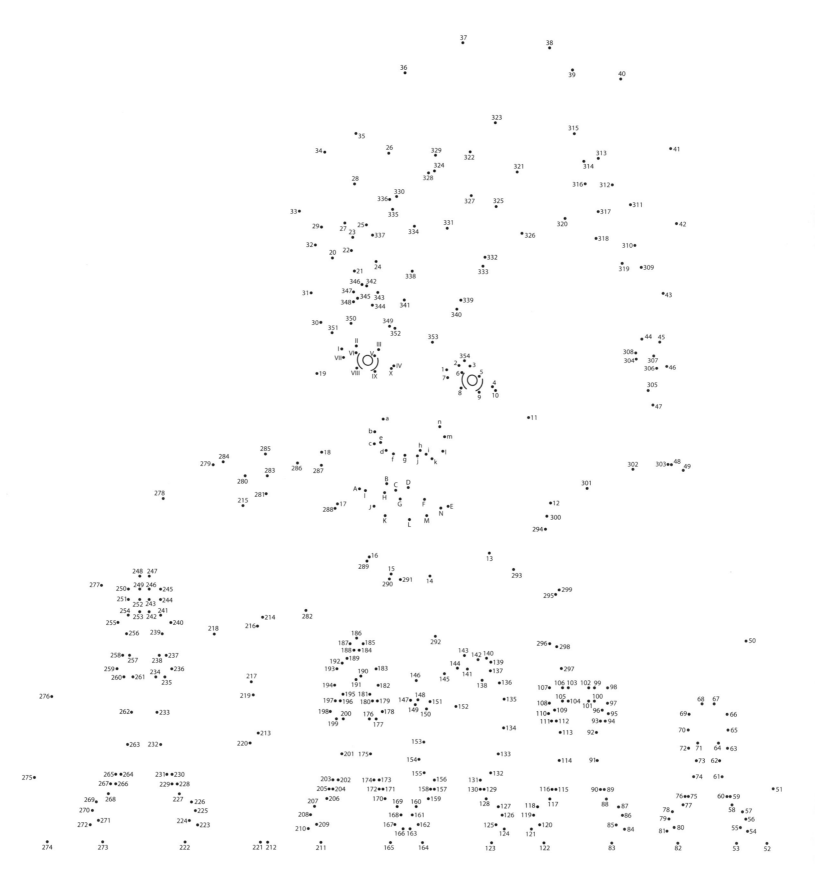

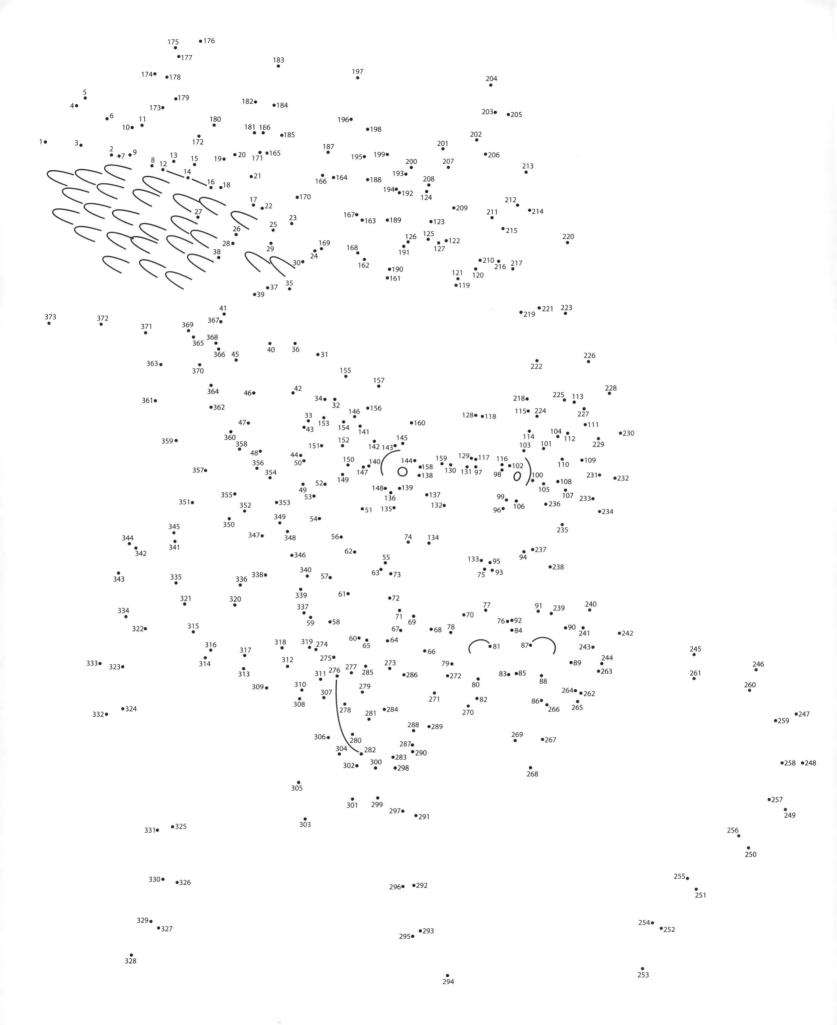

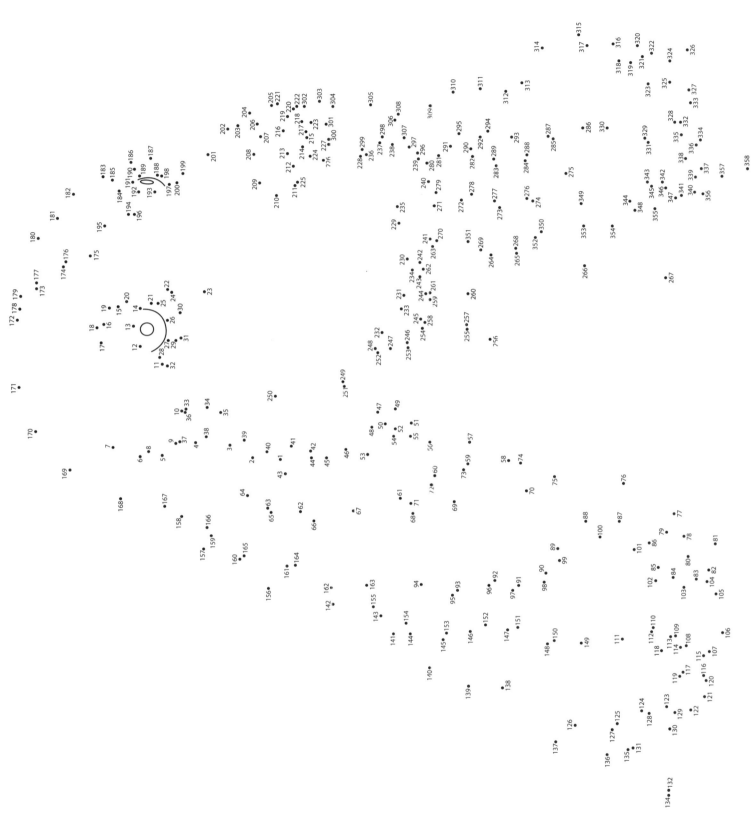

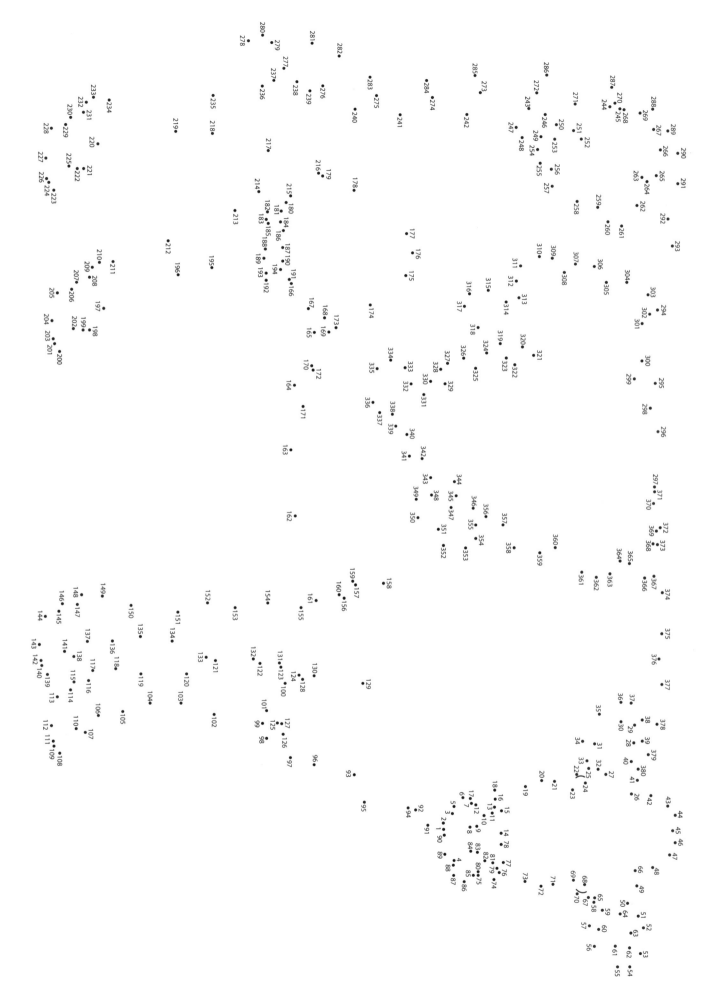

48

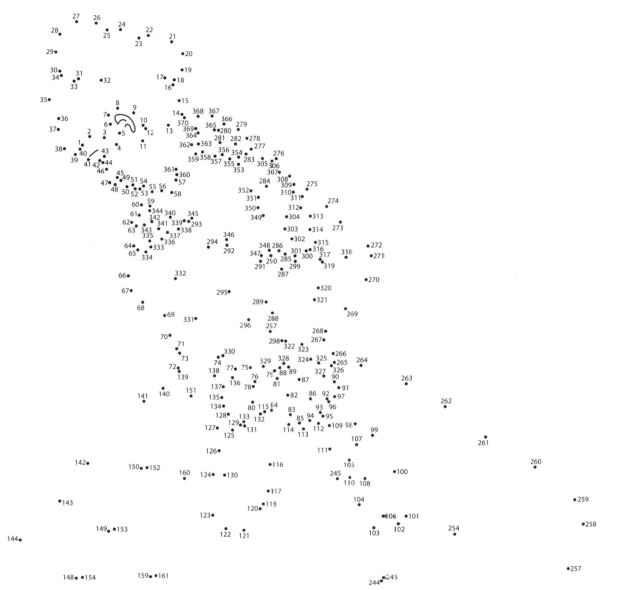

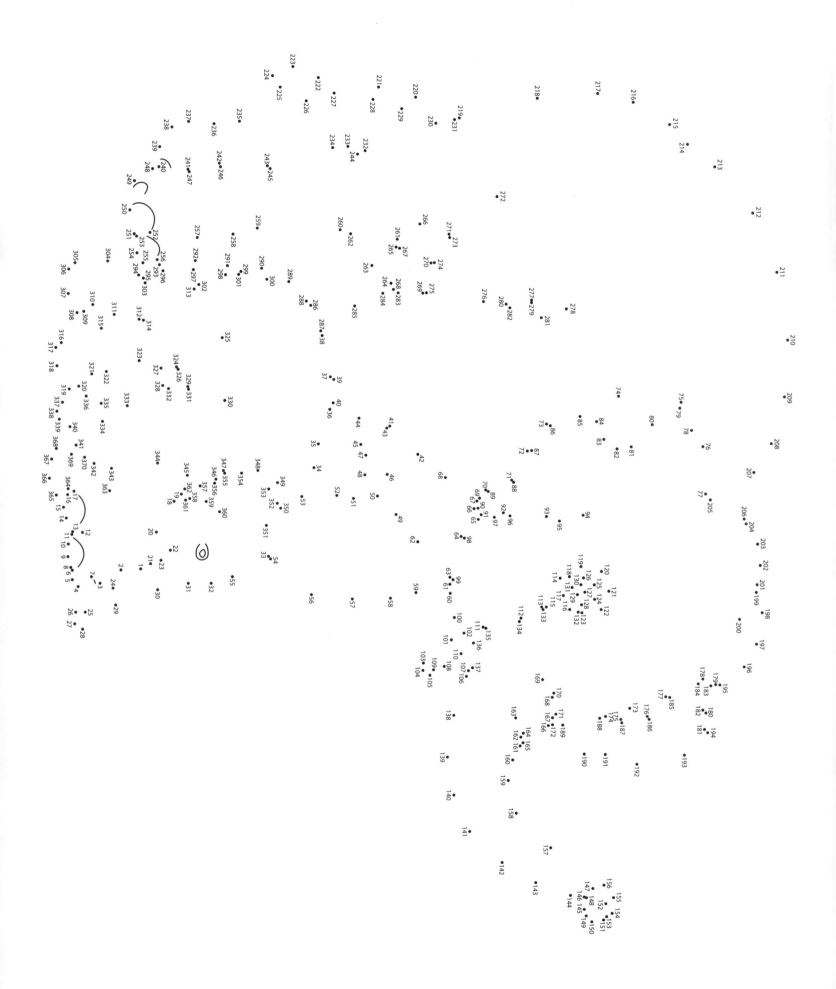

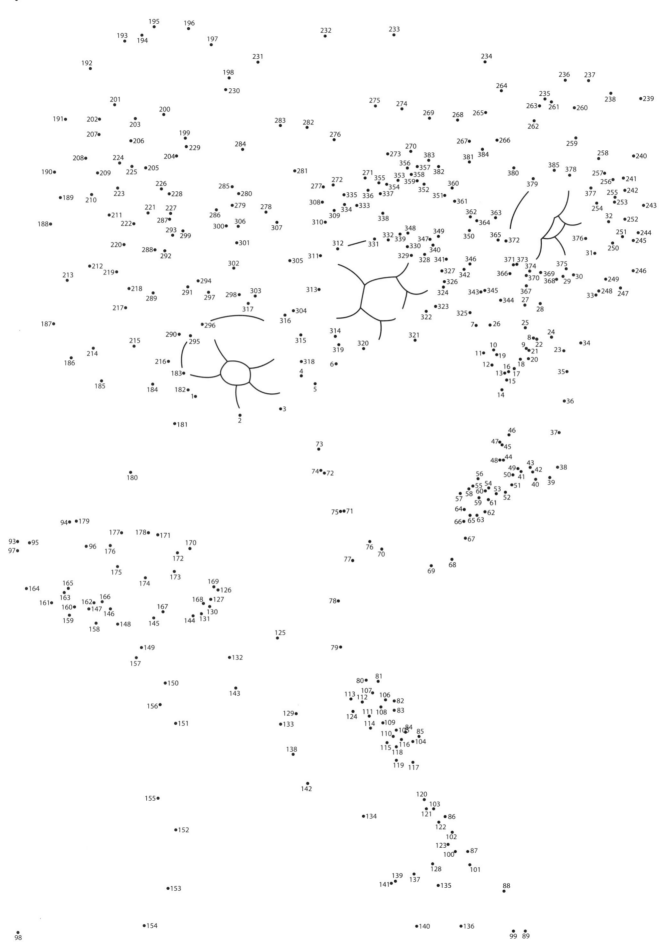

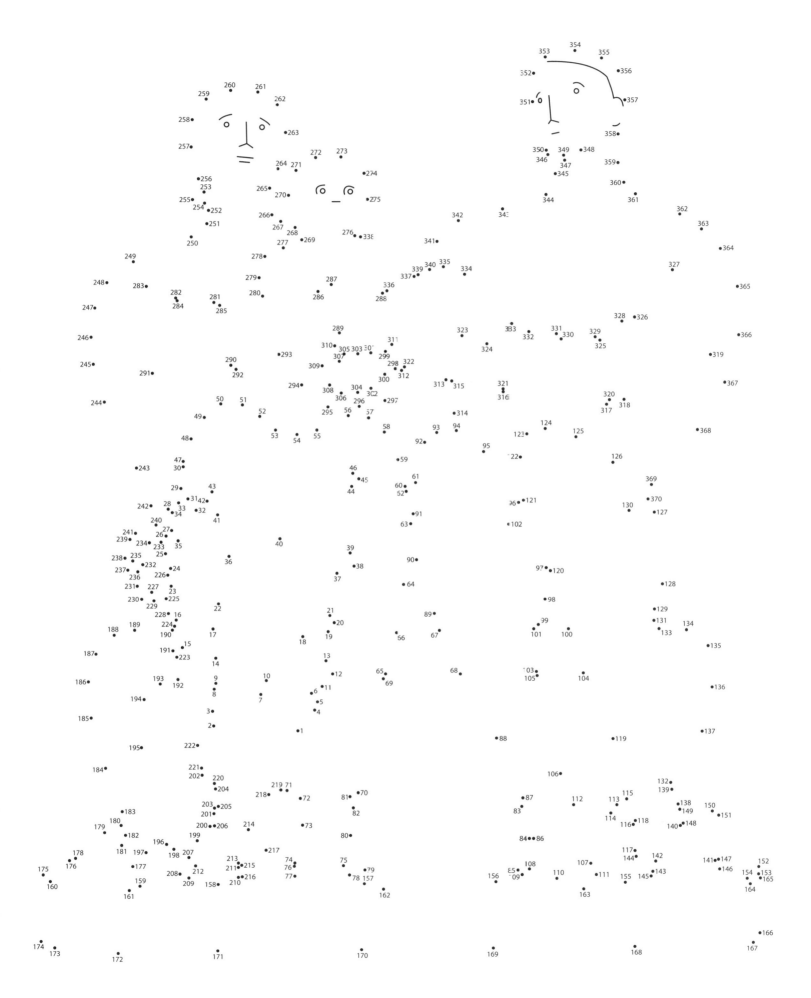

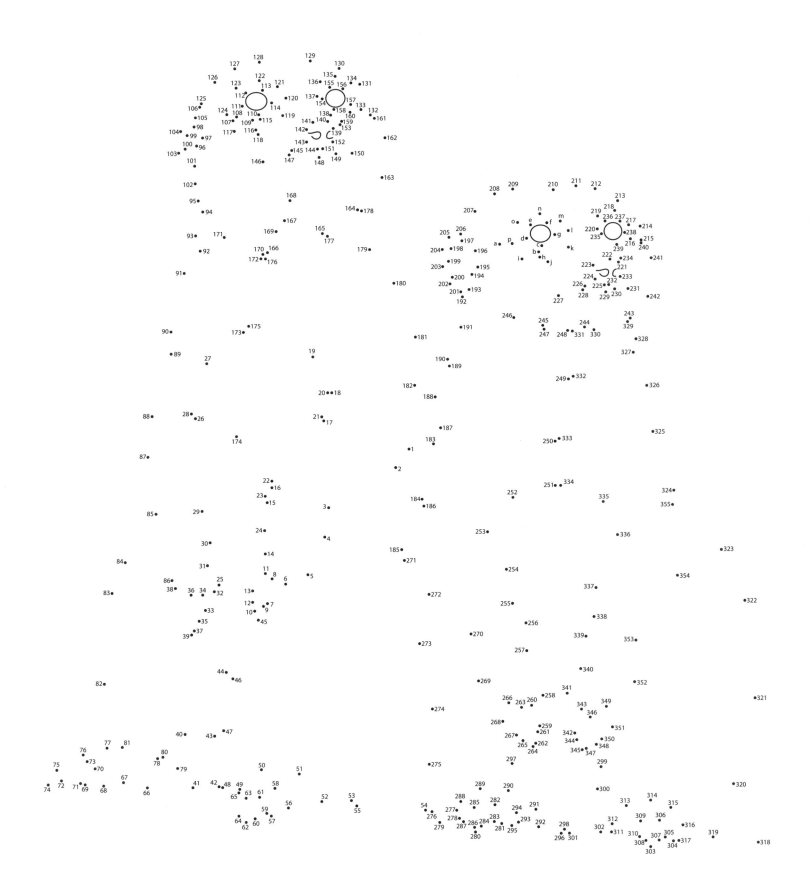

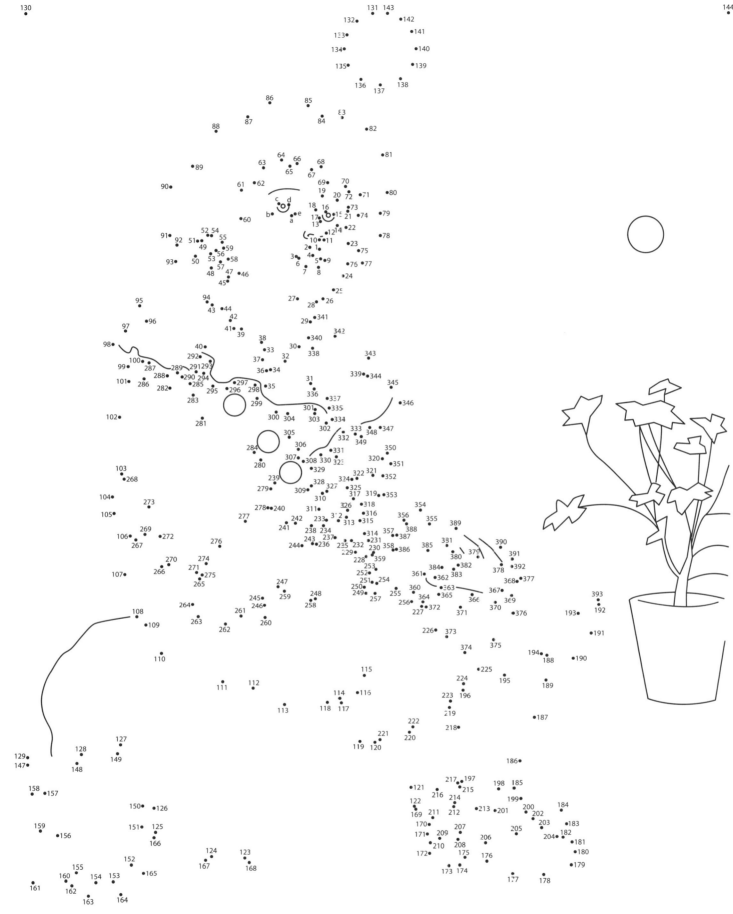

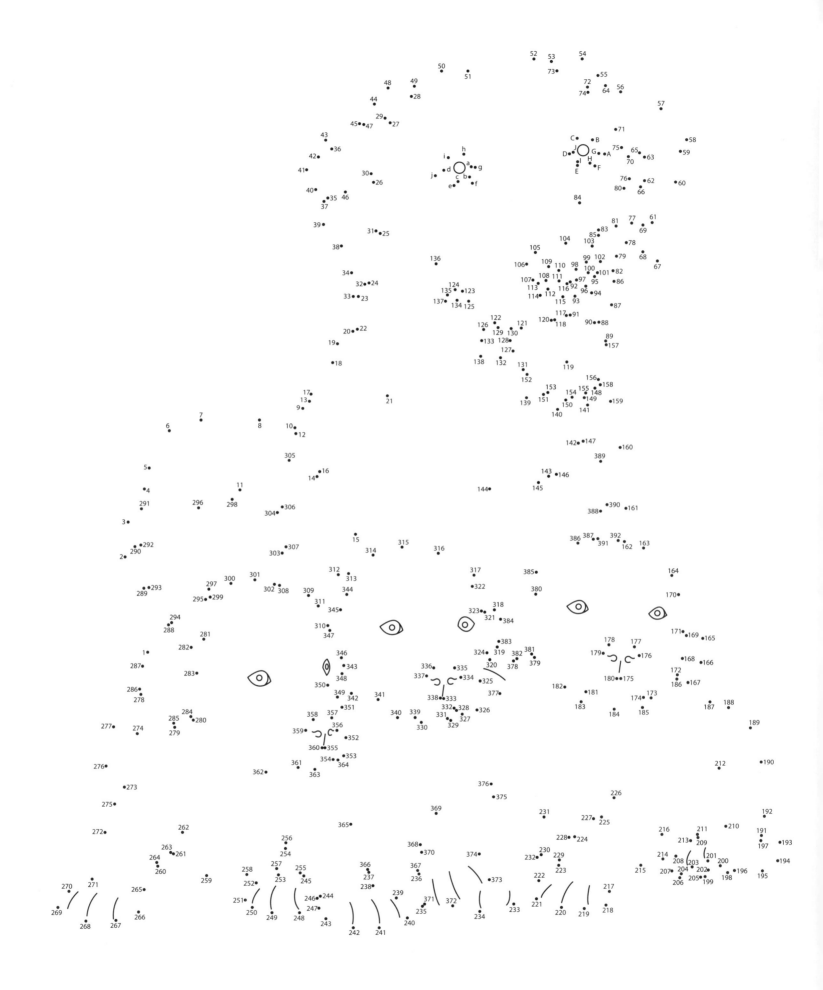

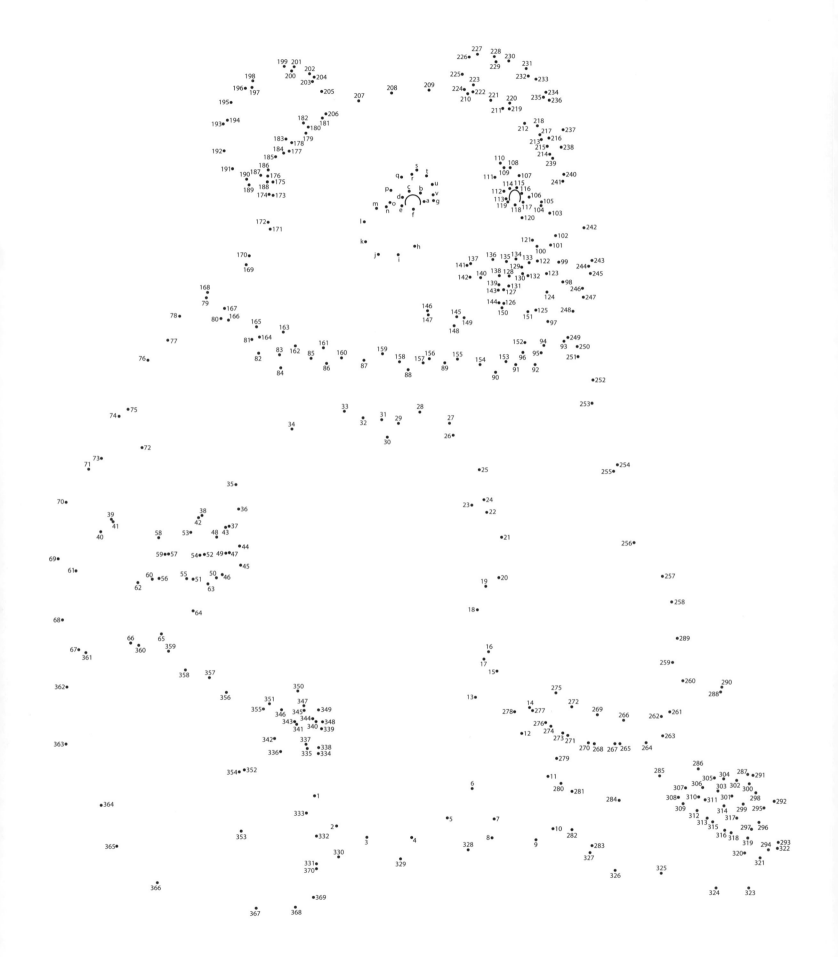

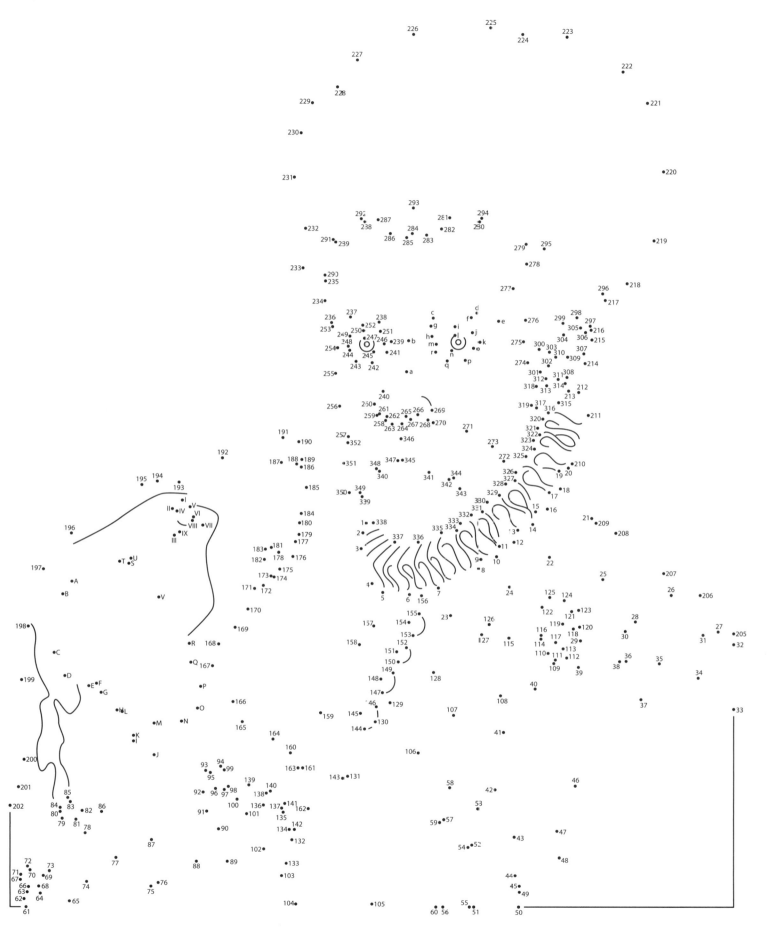

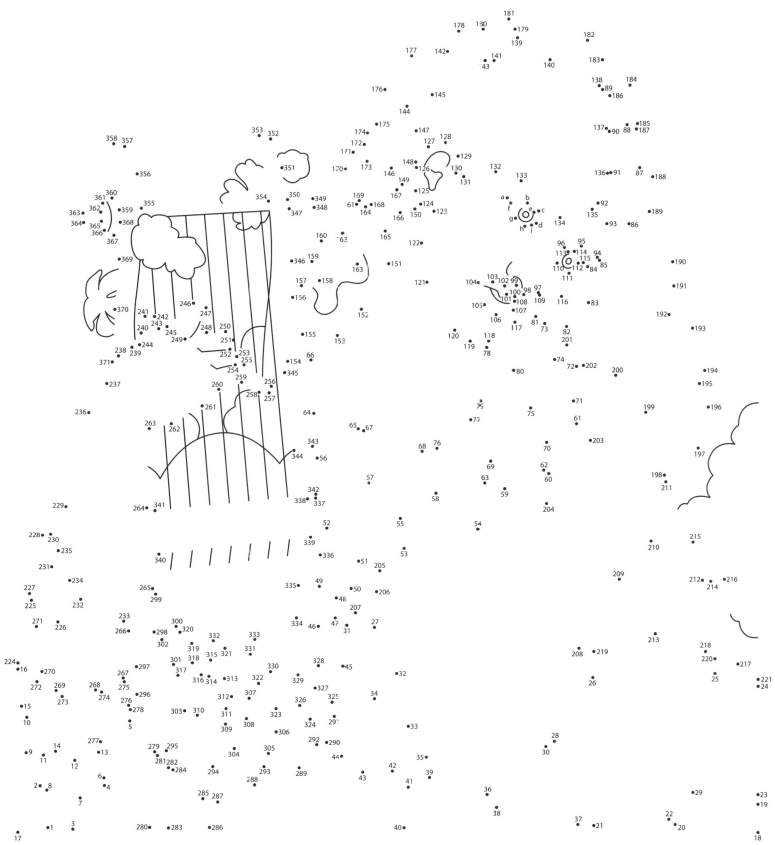

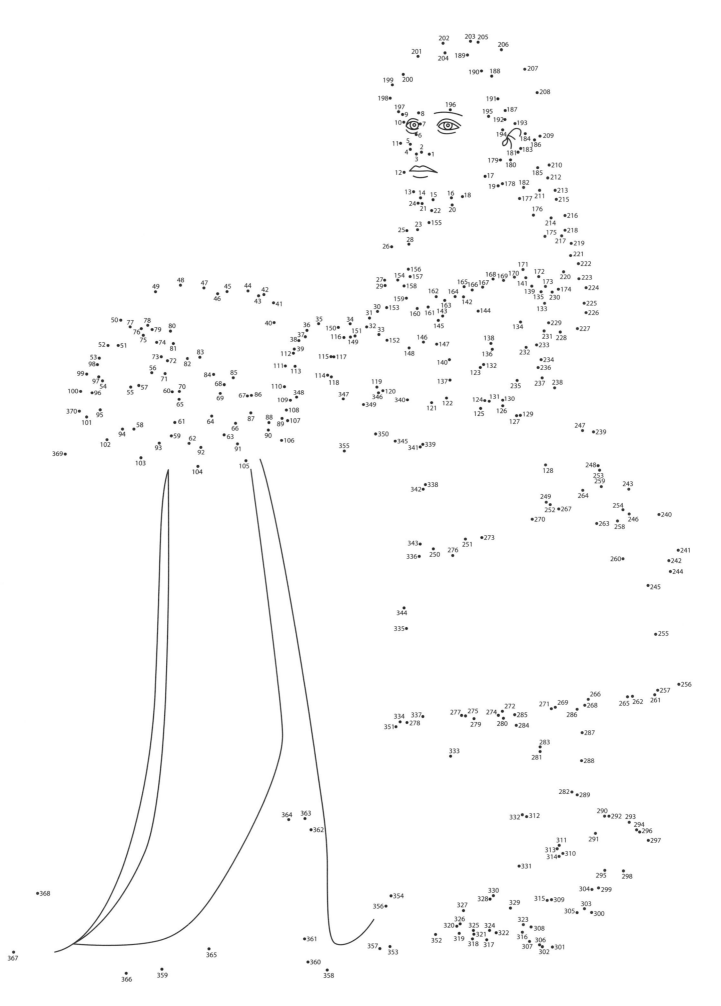

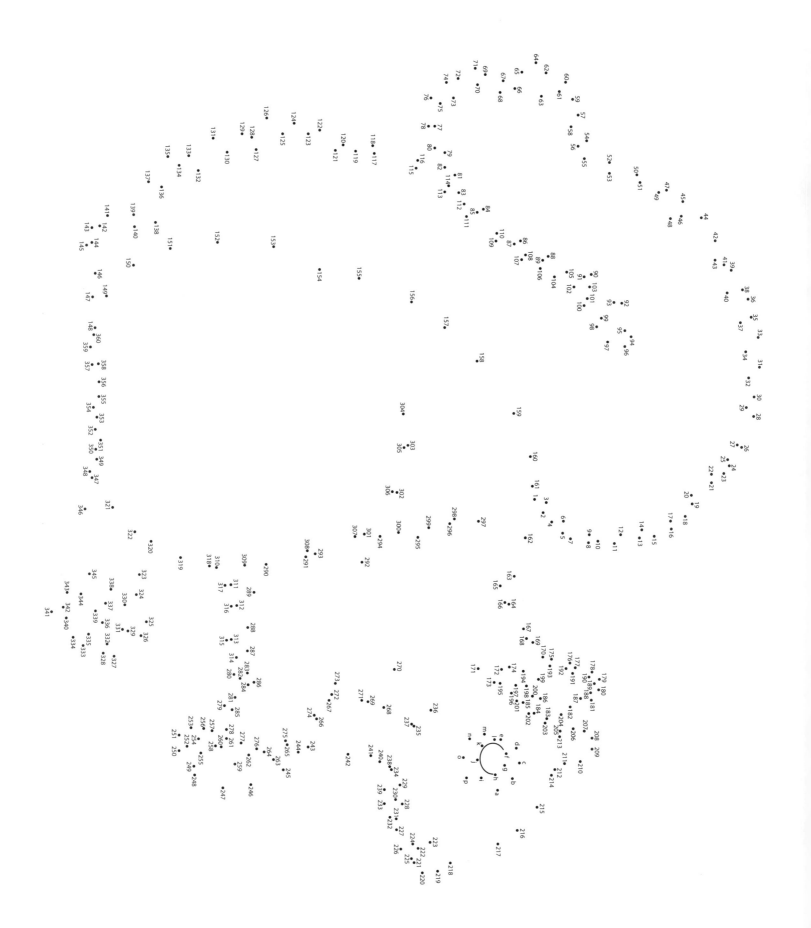

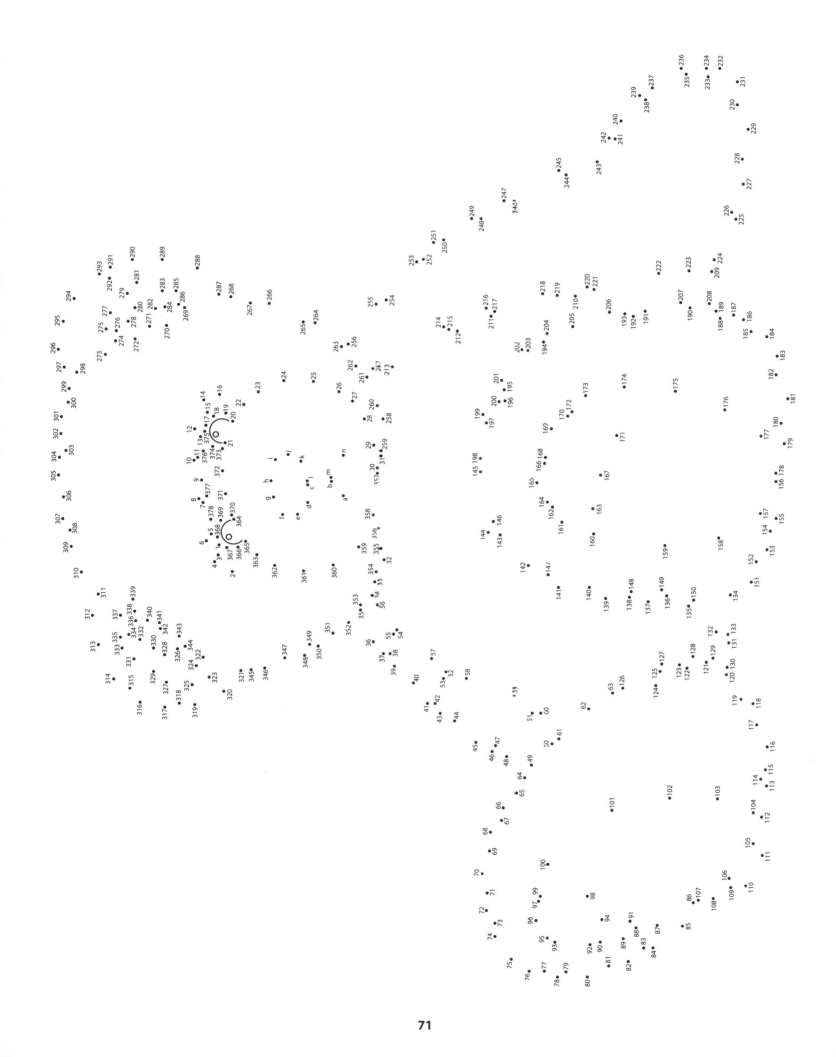

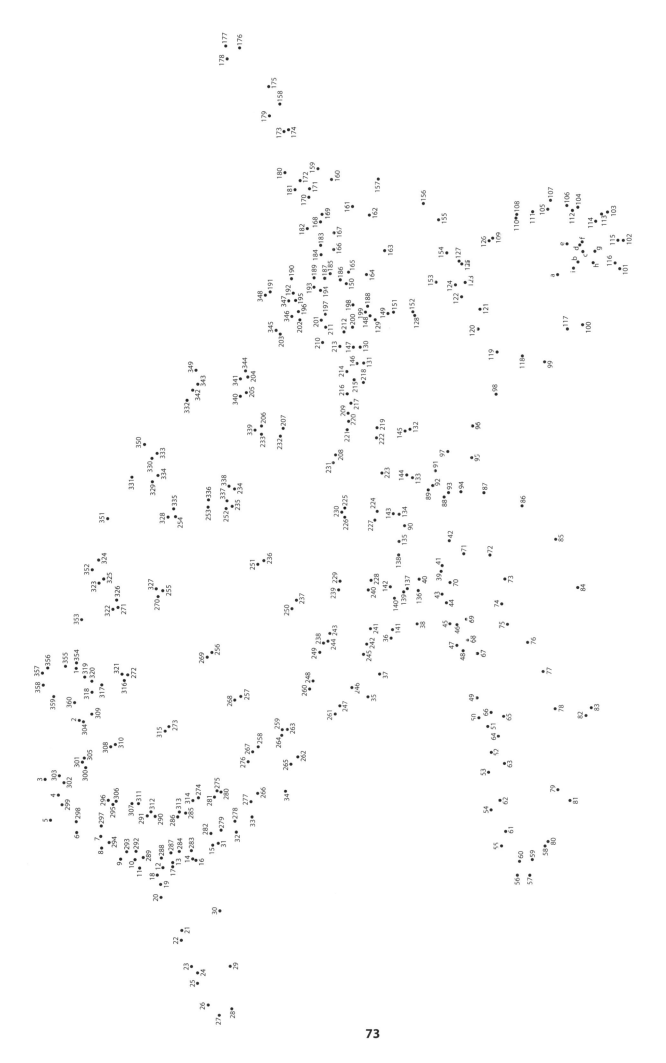

73

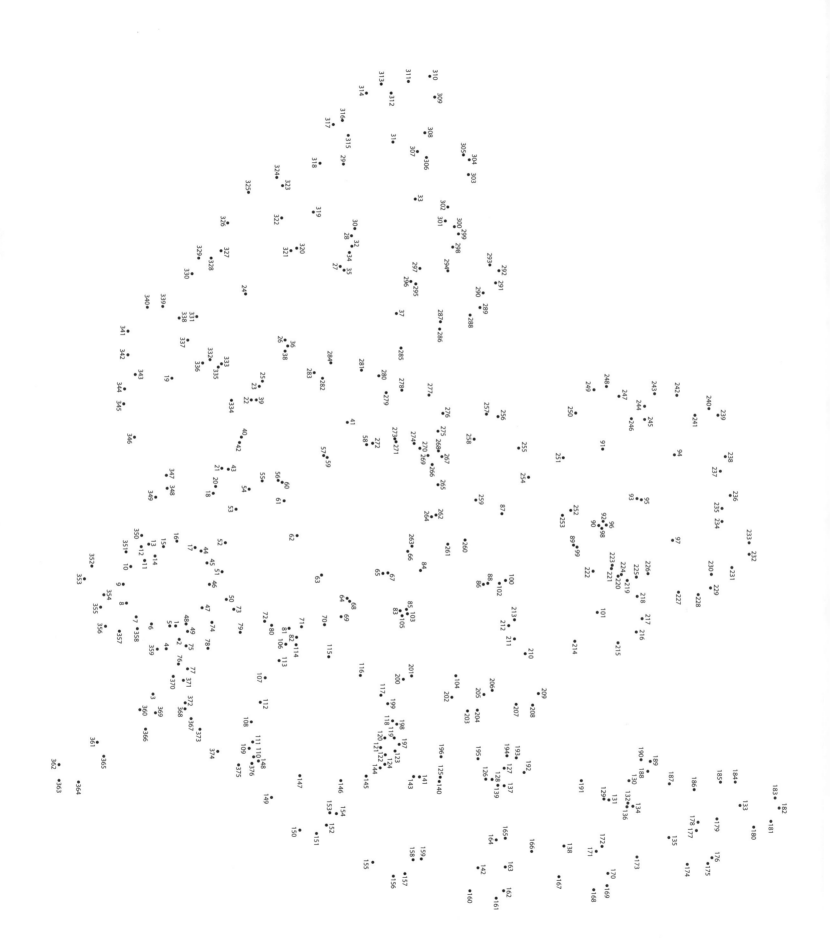

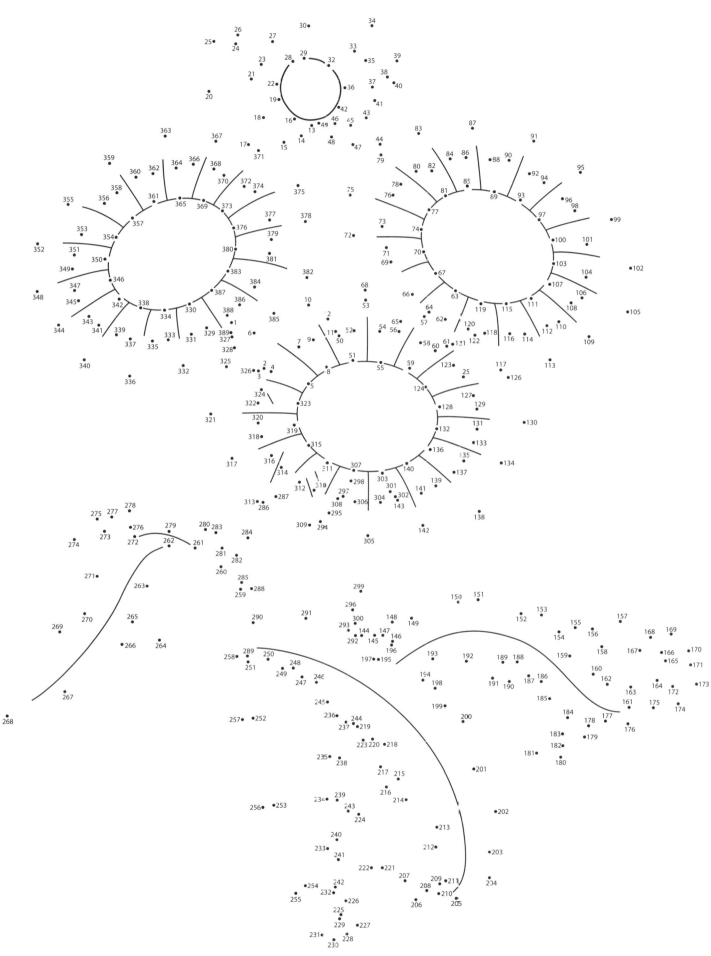

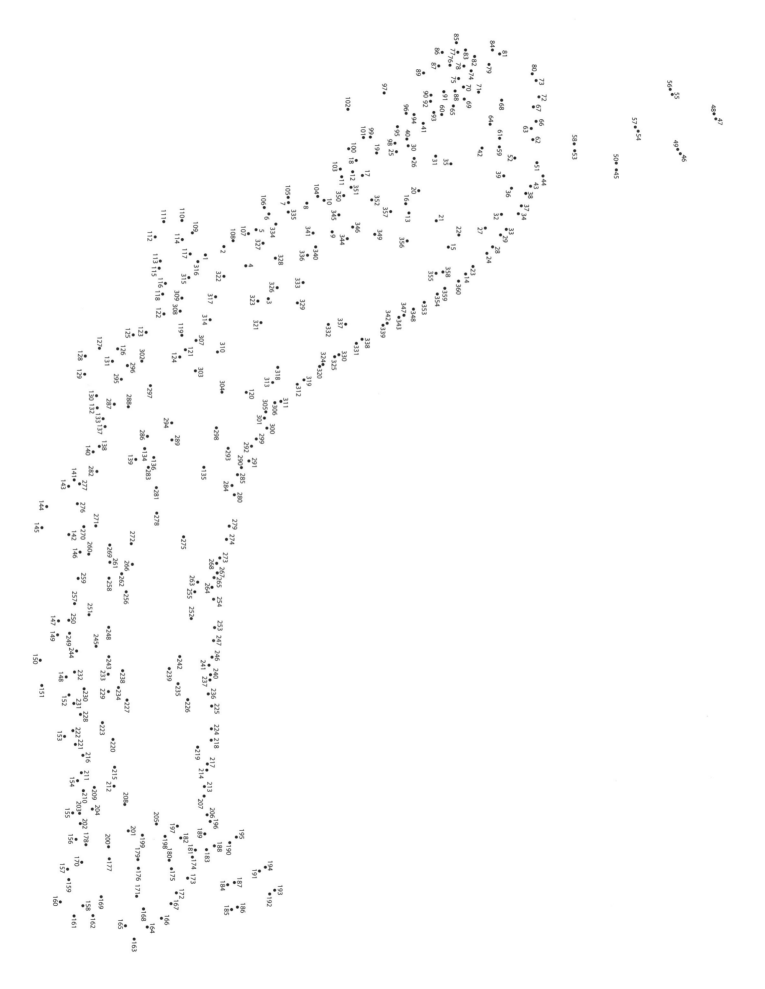

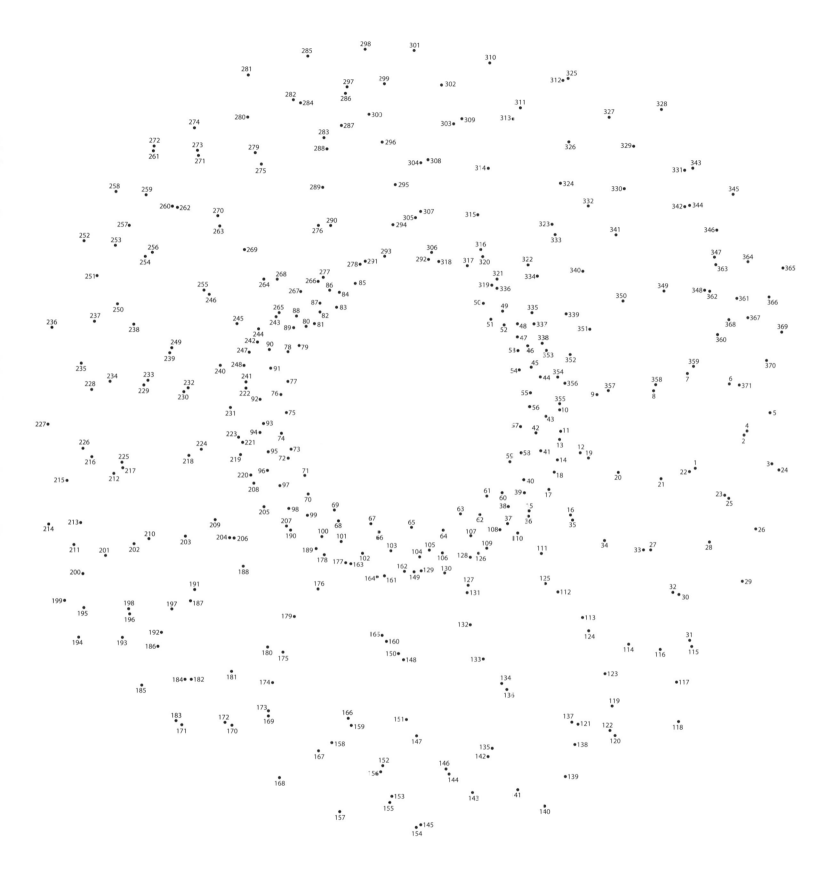

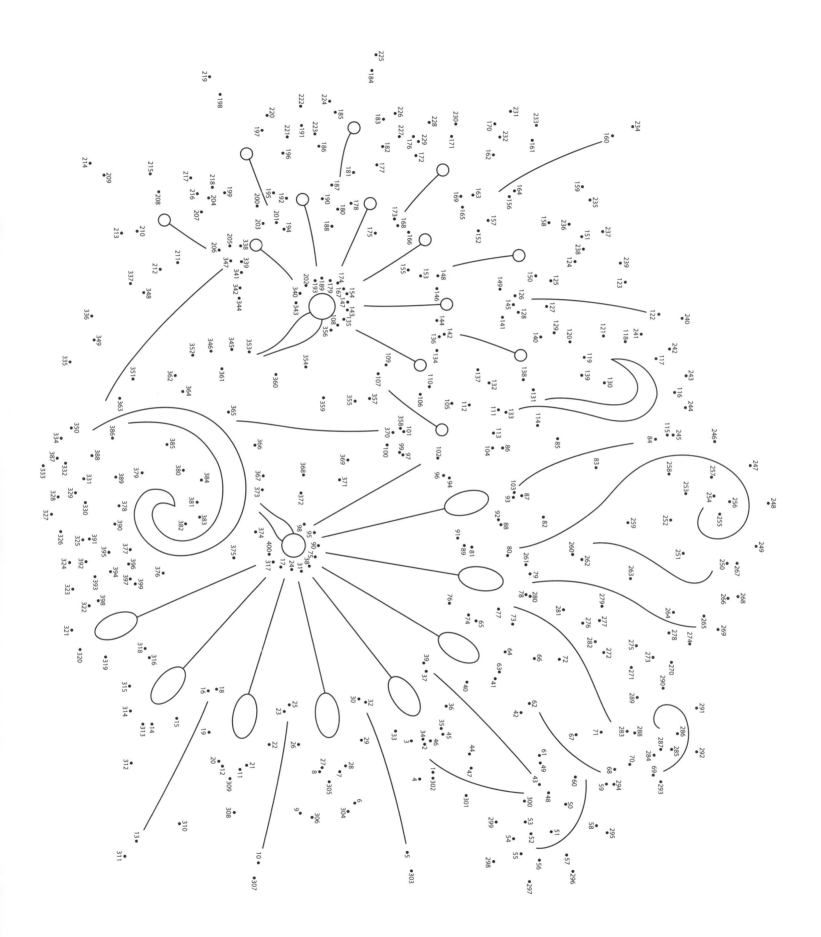

80

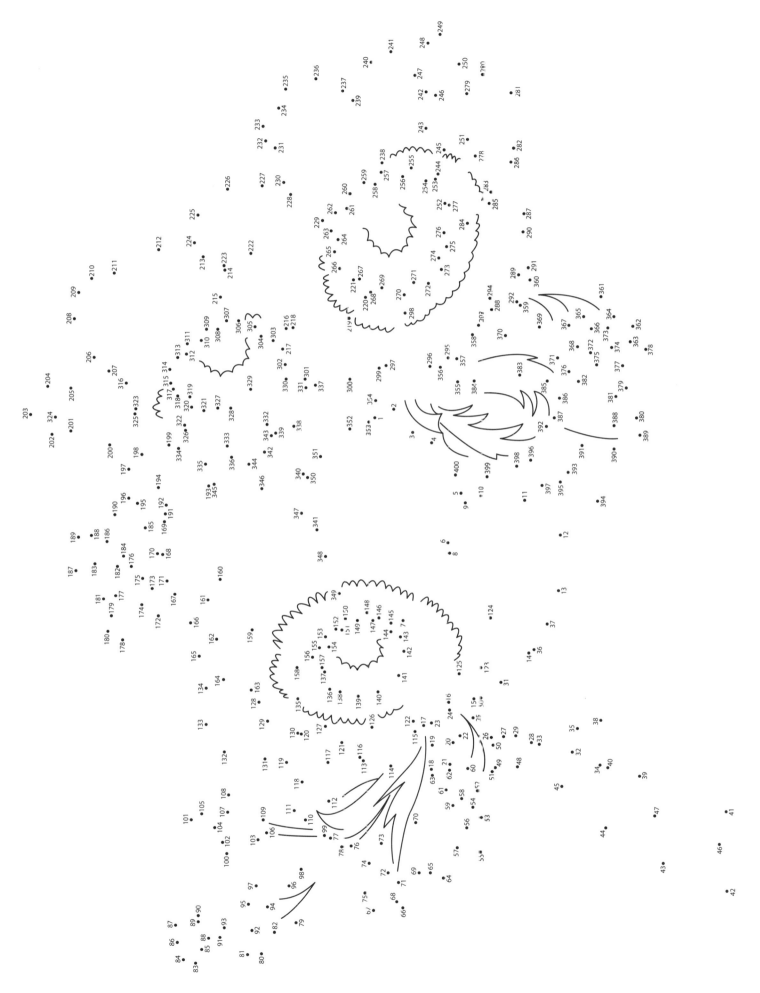

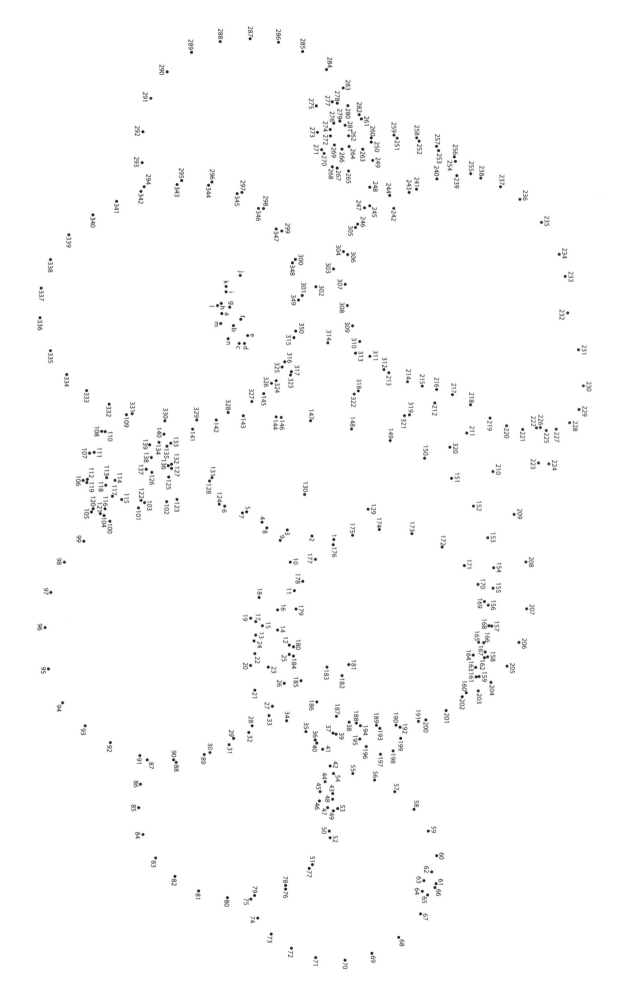

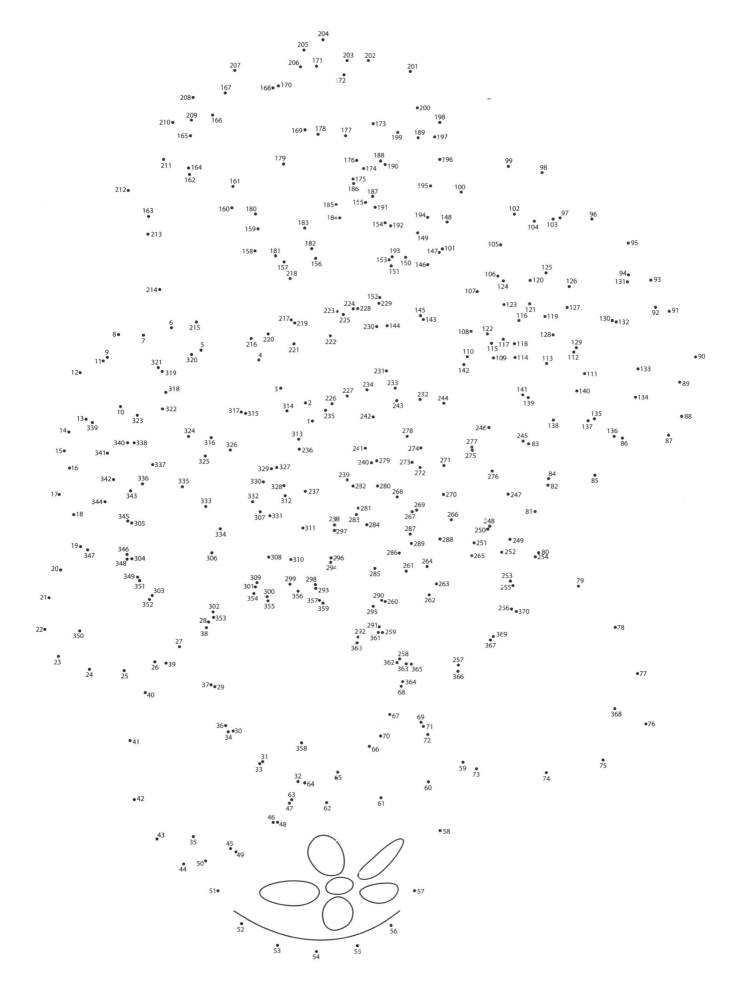

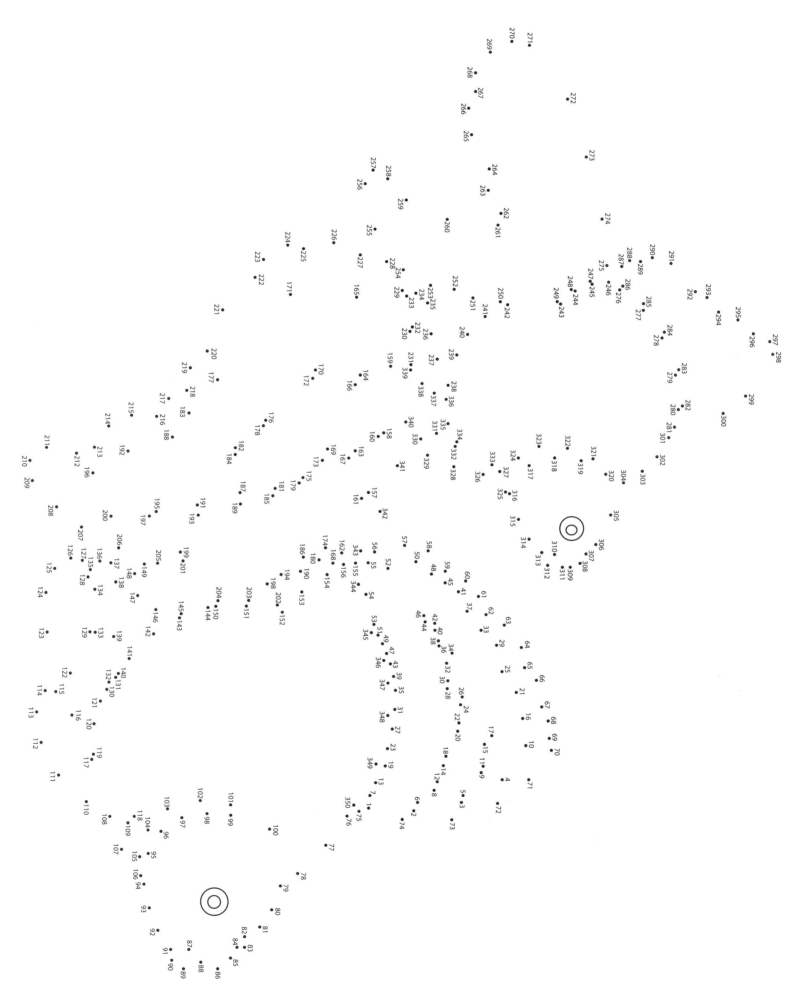

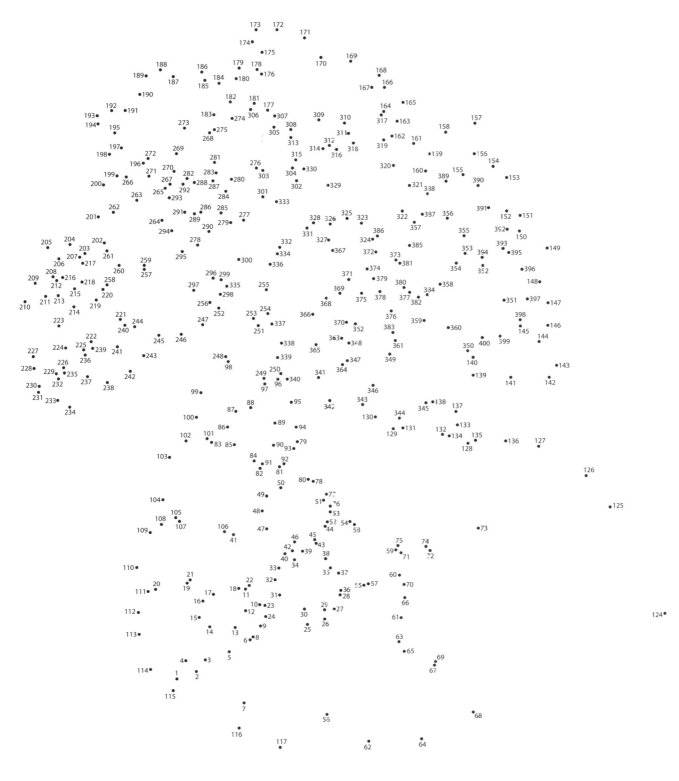

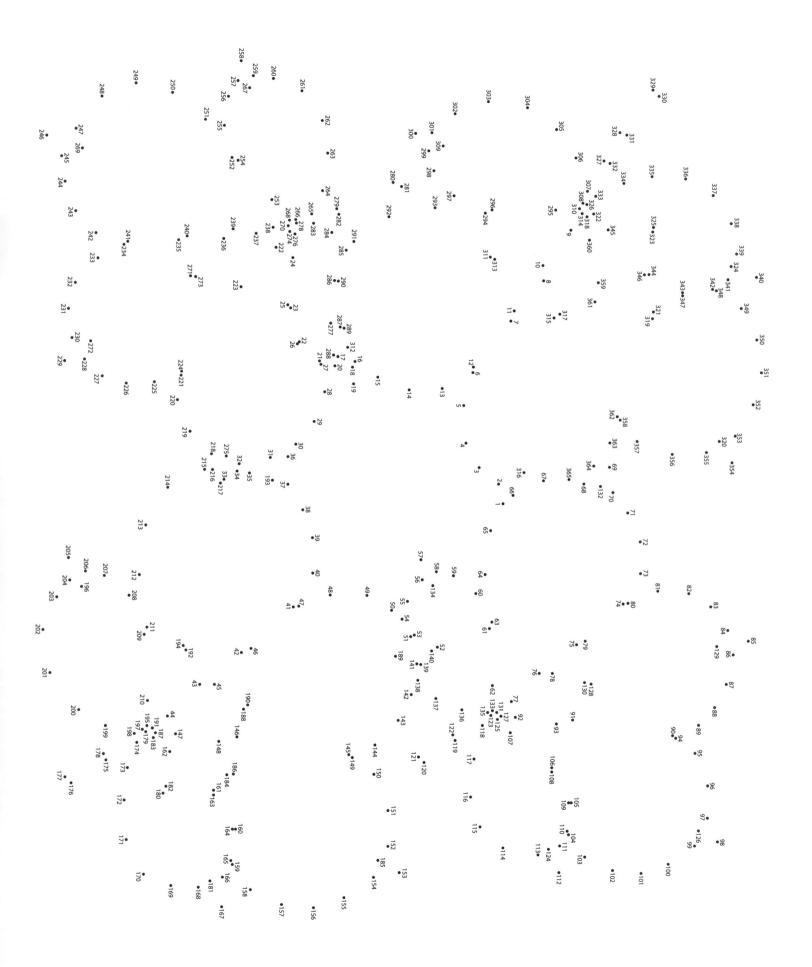

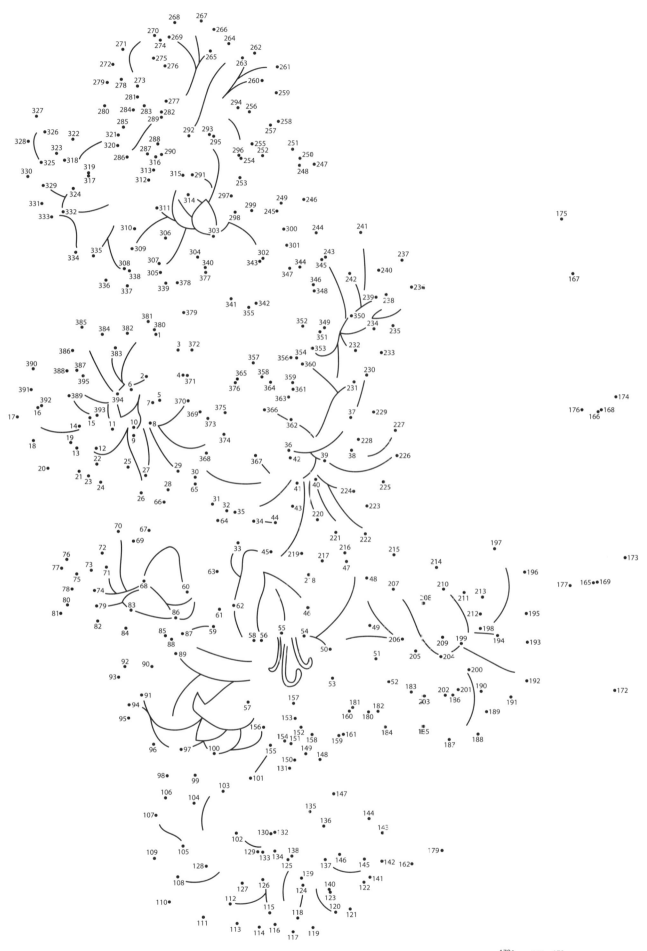

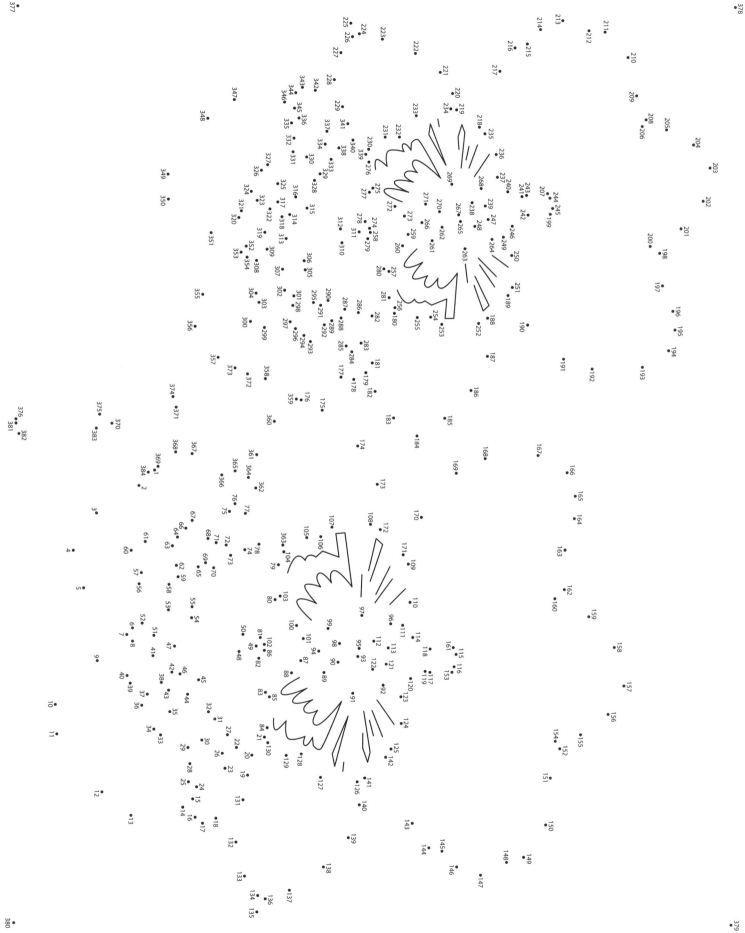

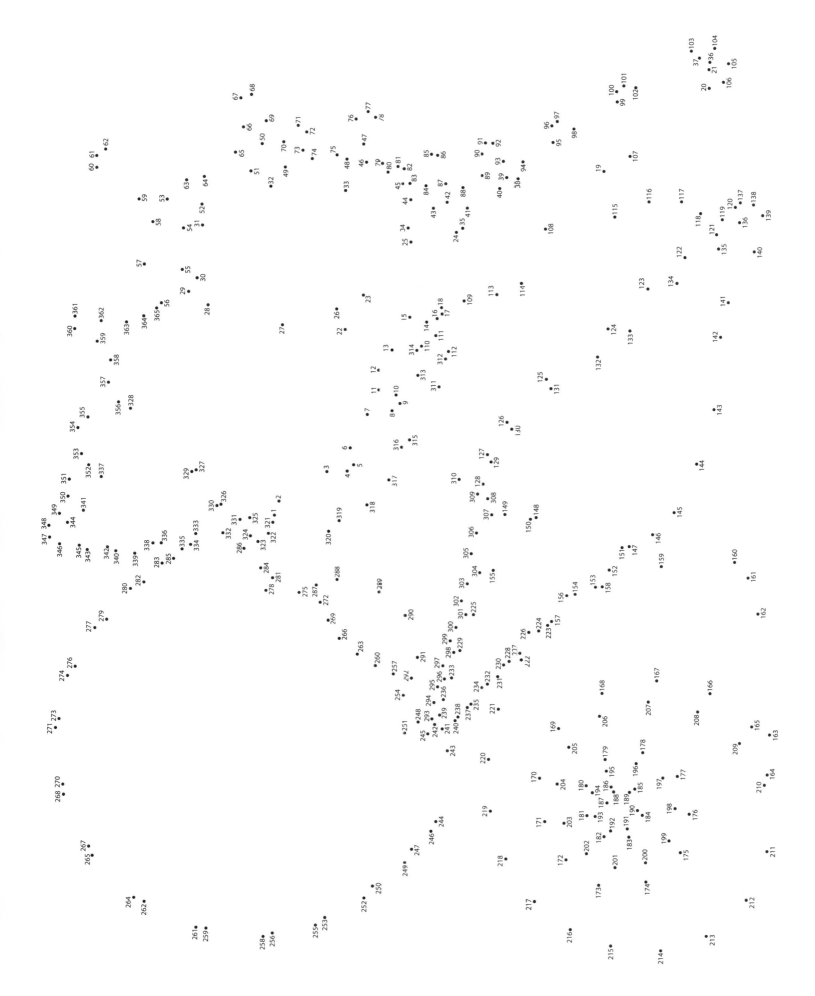

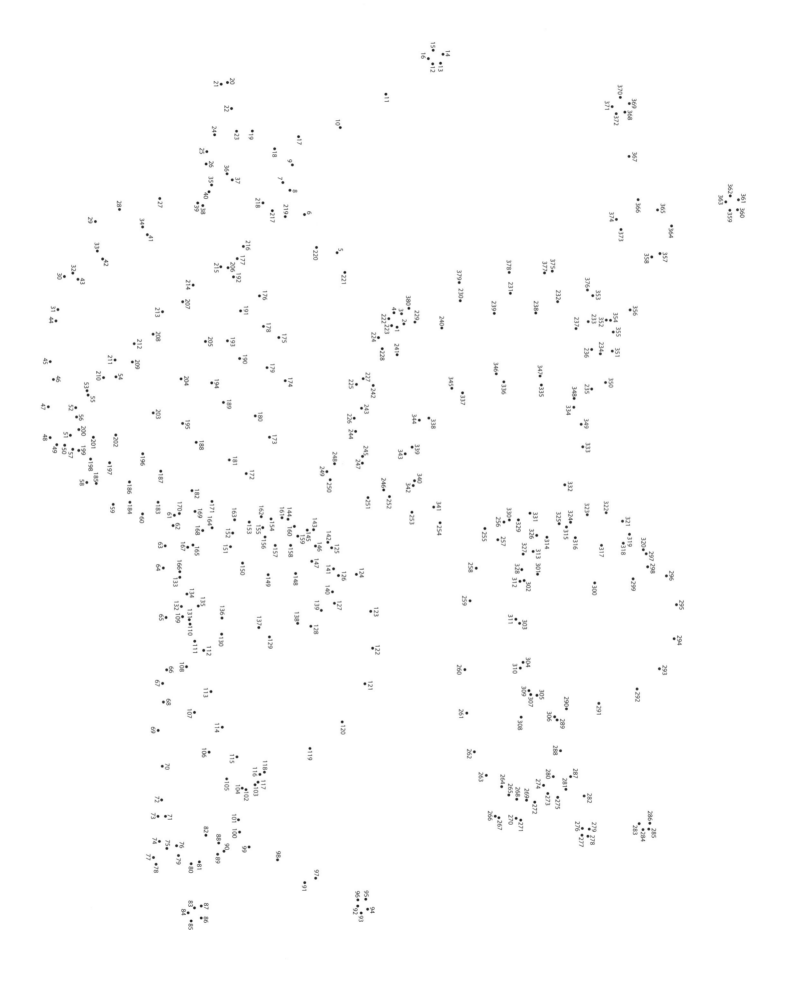

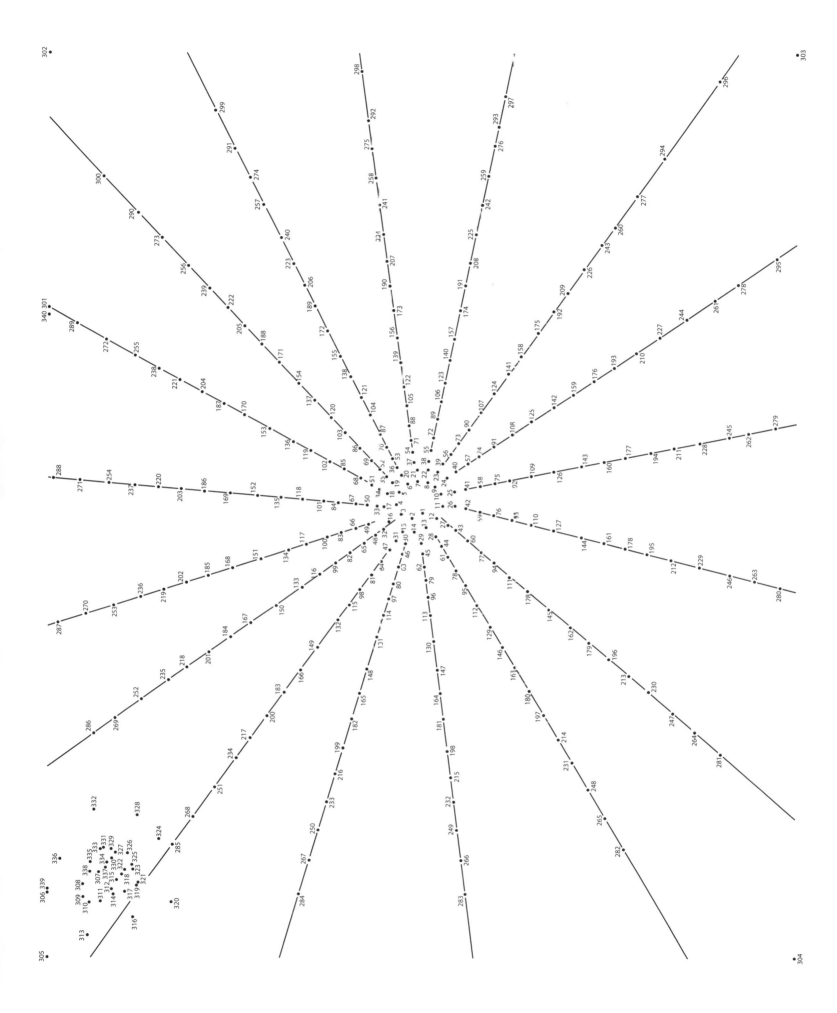

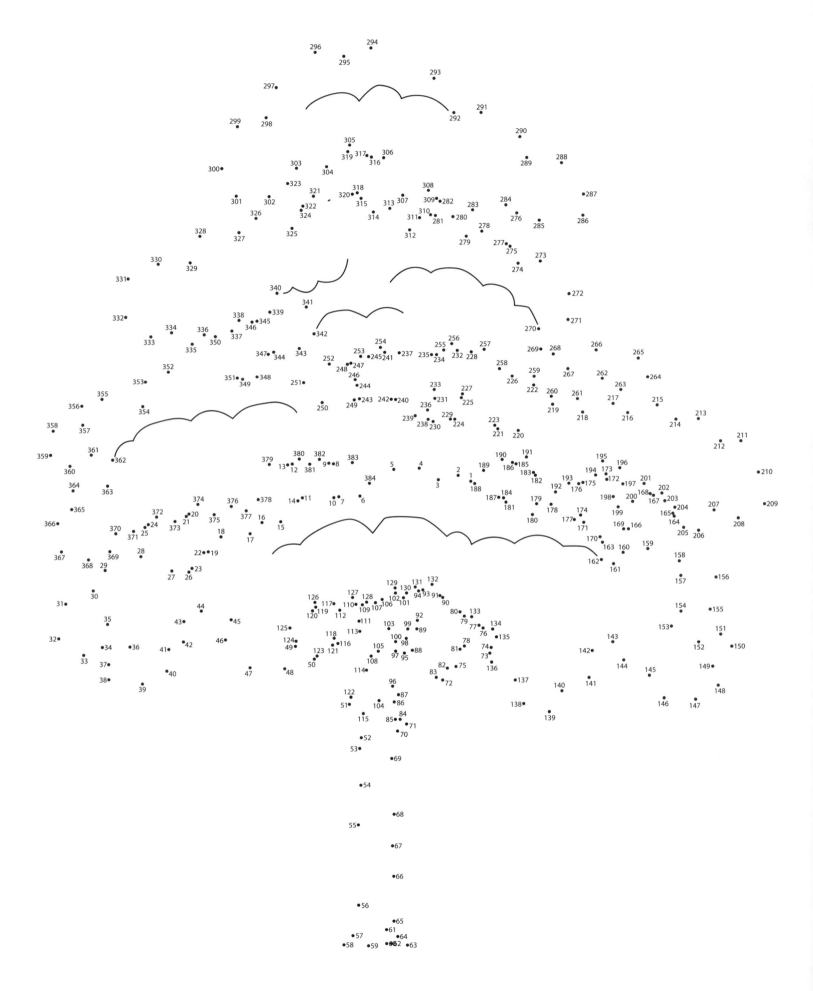

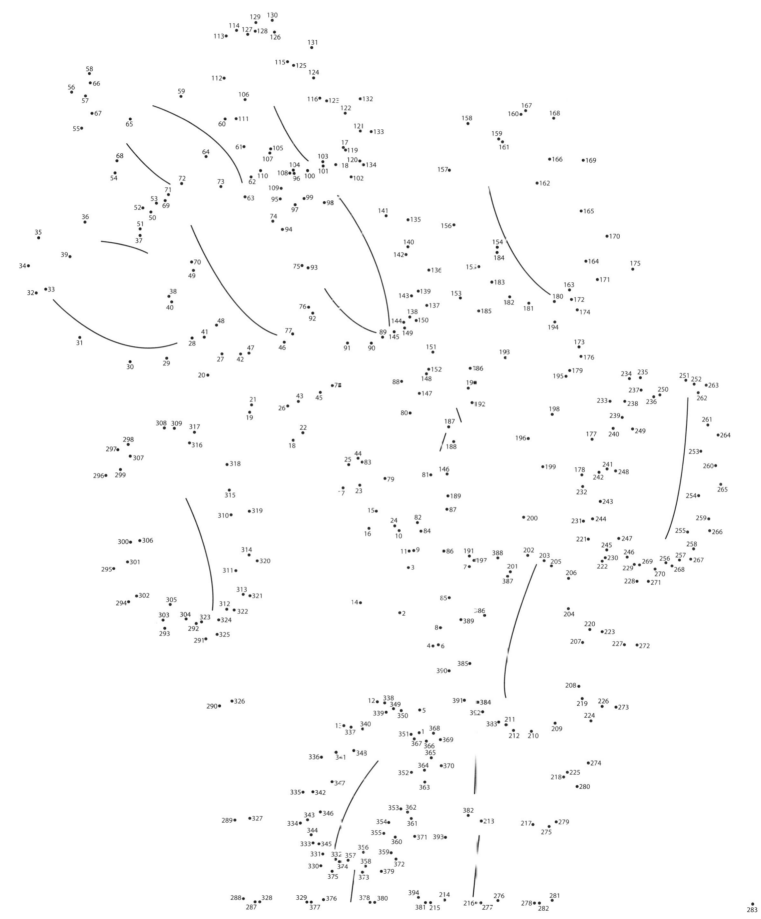

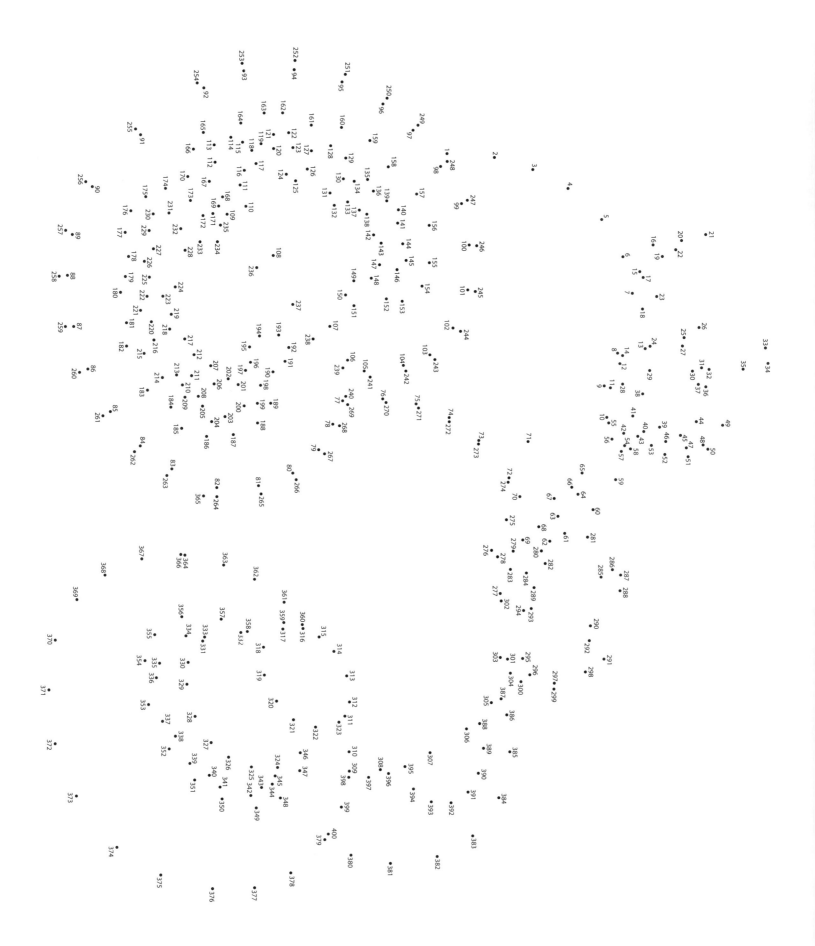

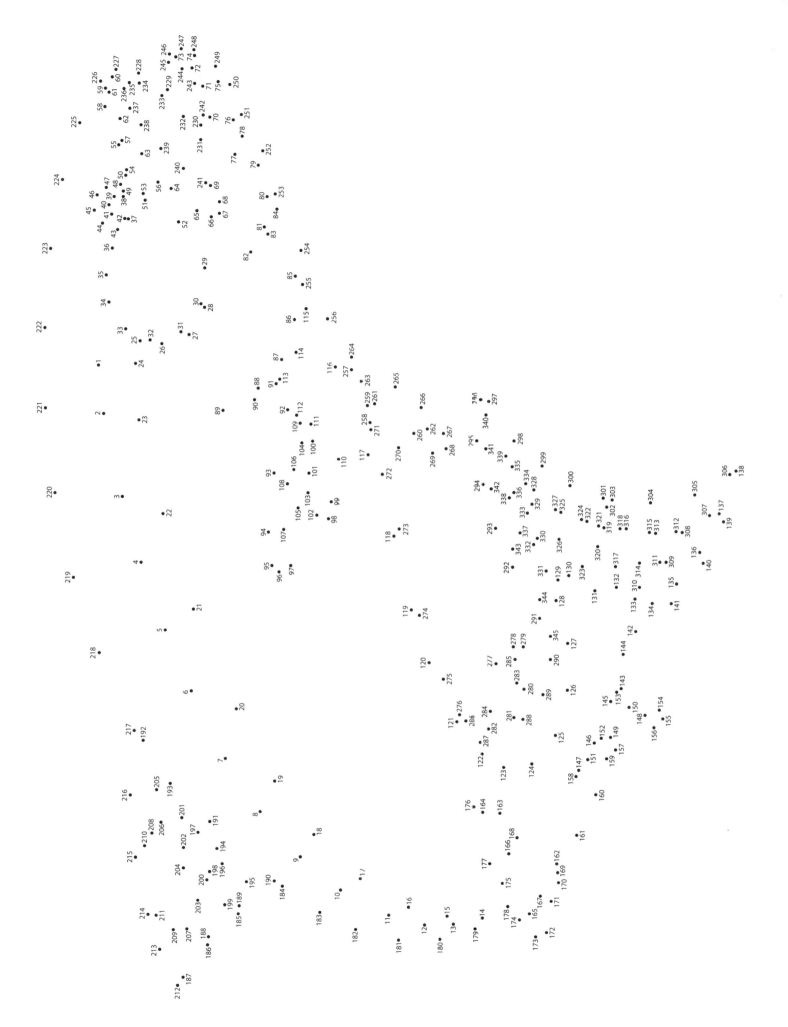

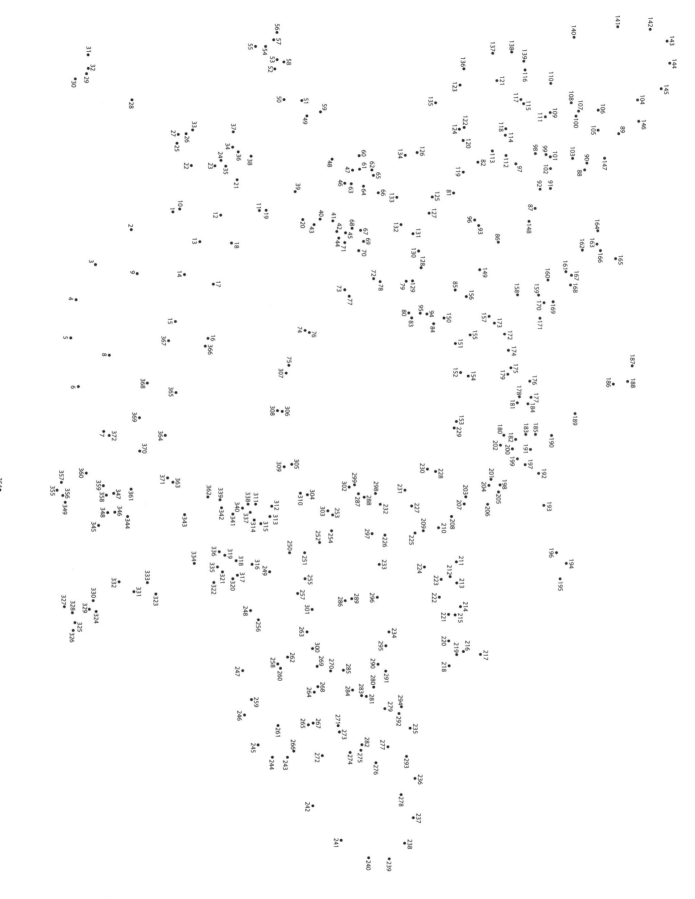

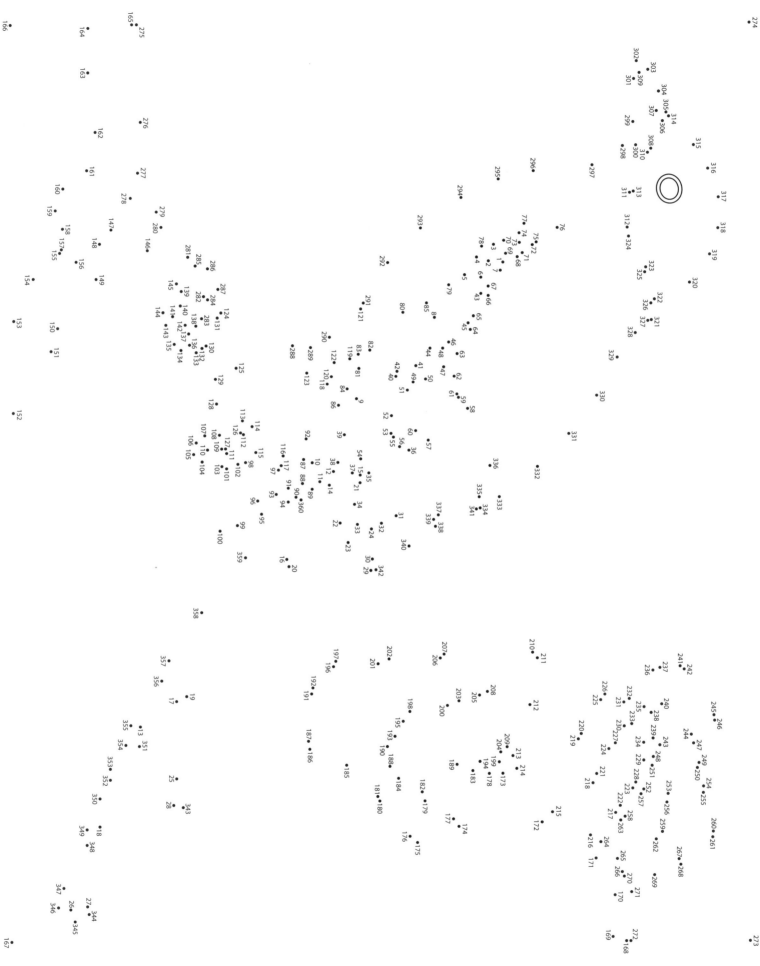

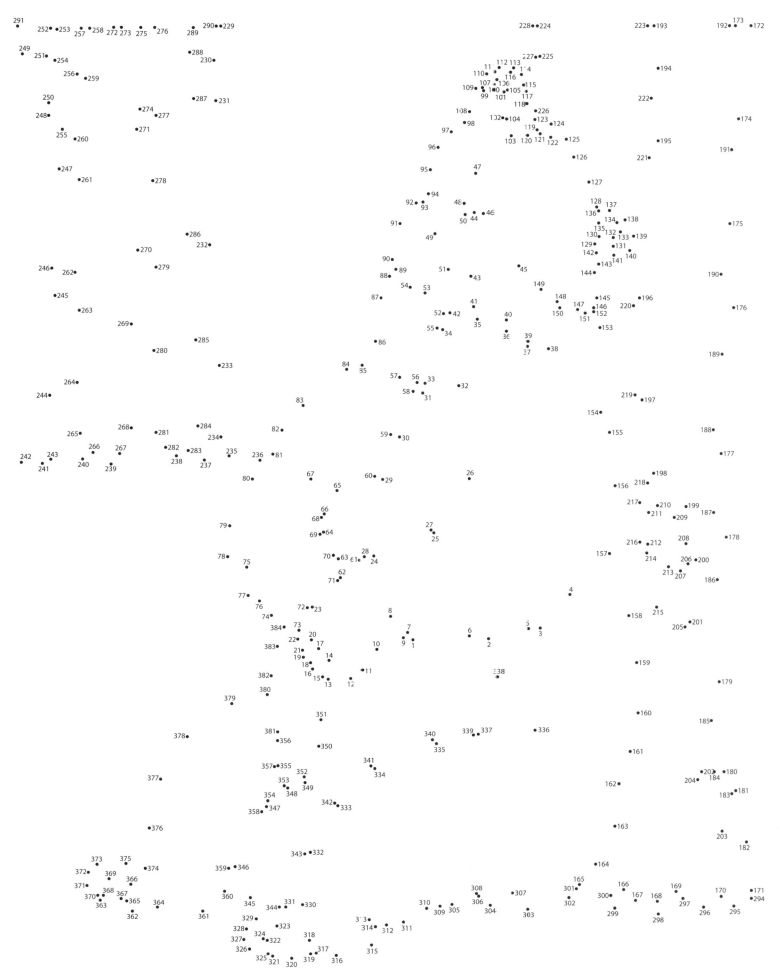

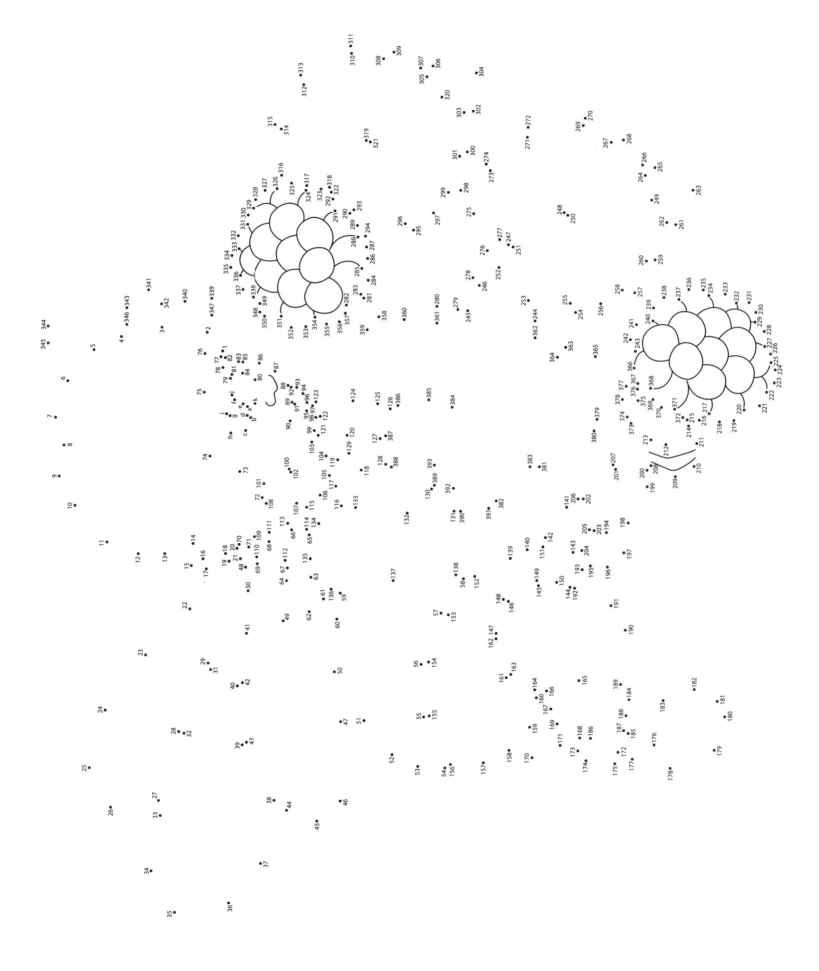

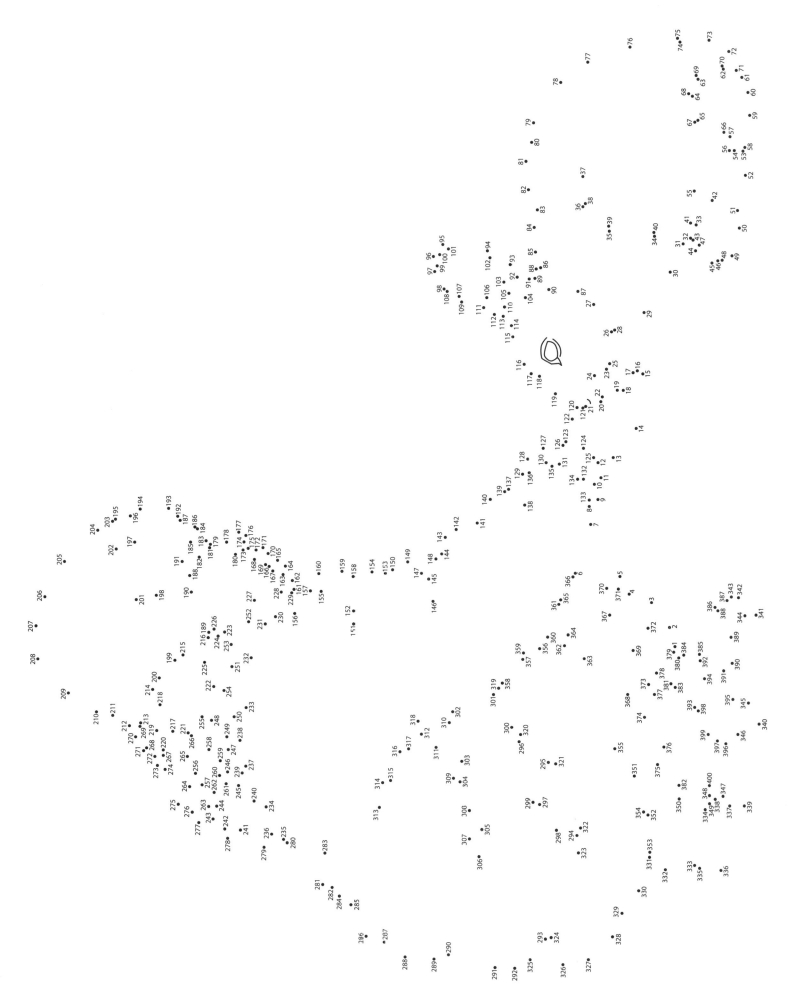

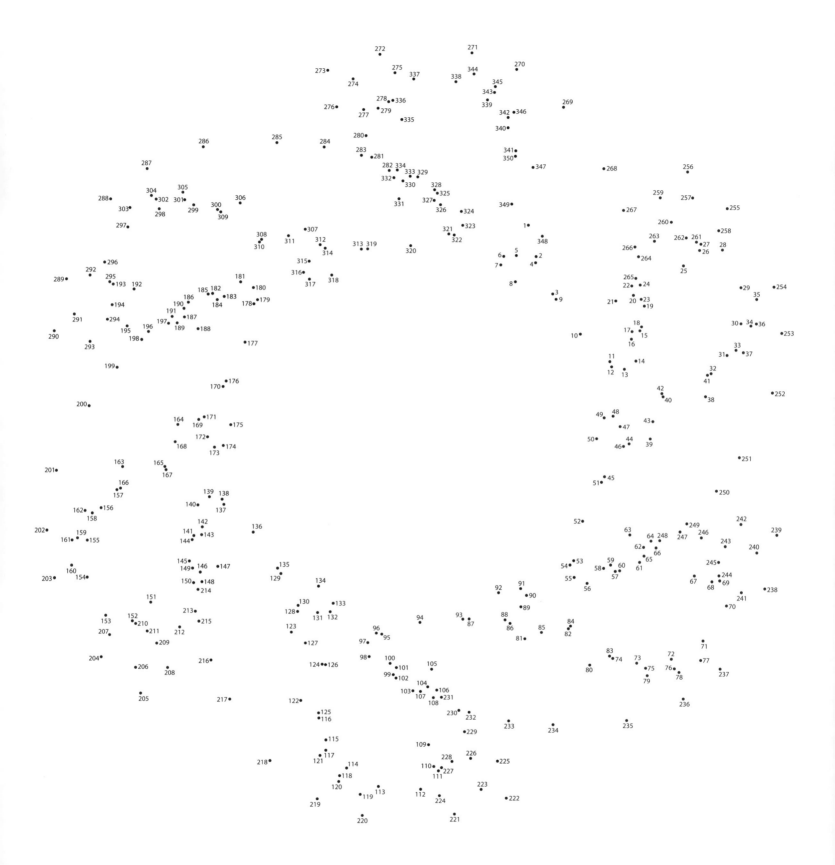

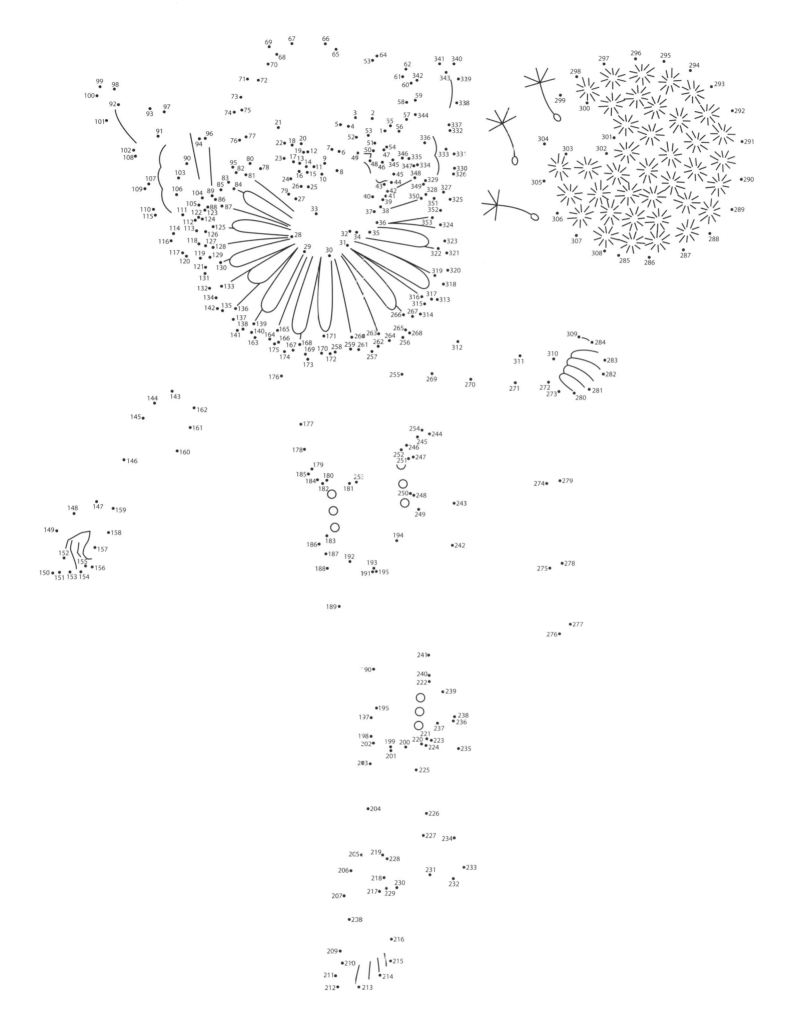

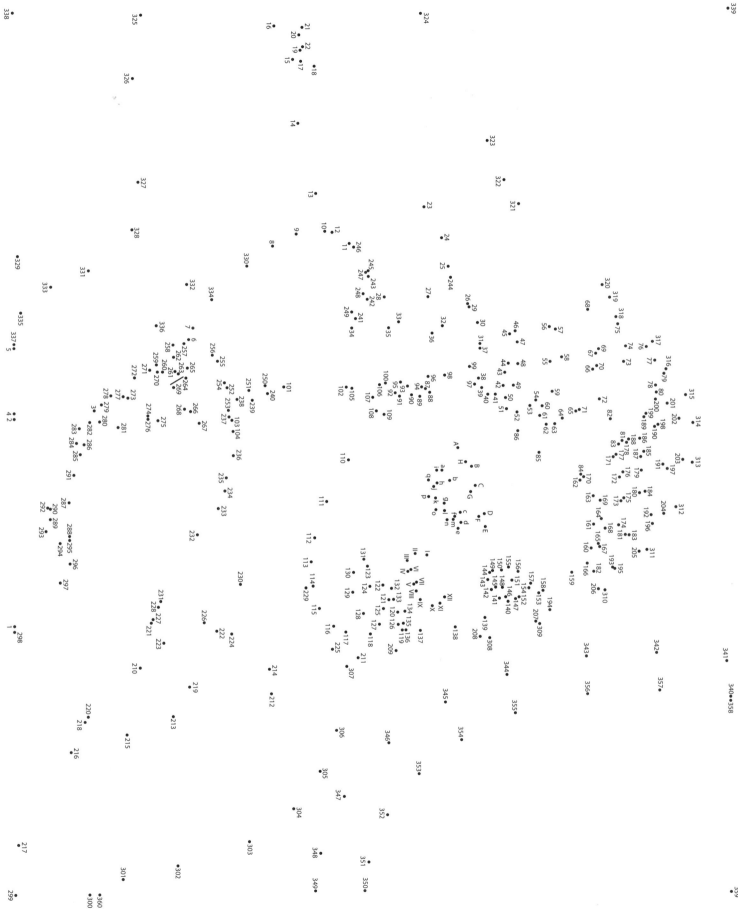

108

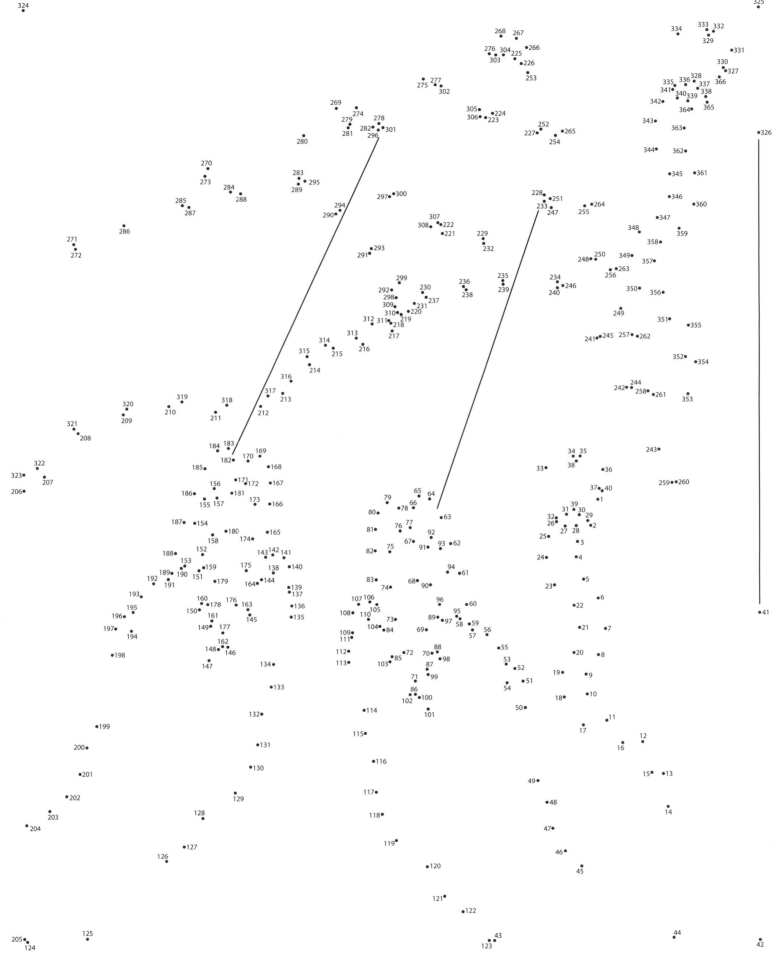

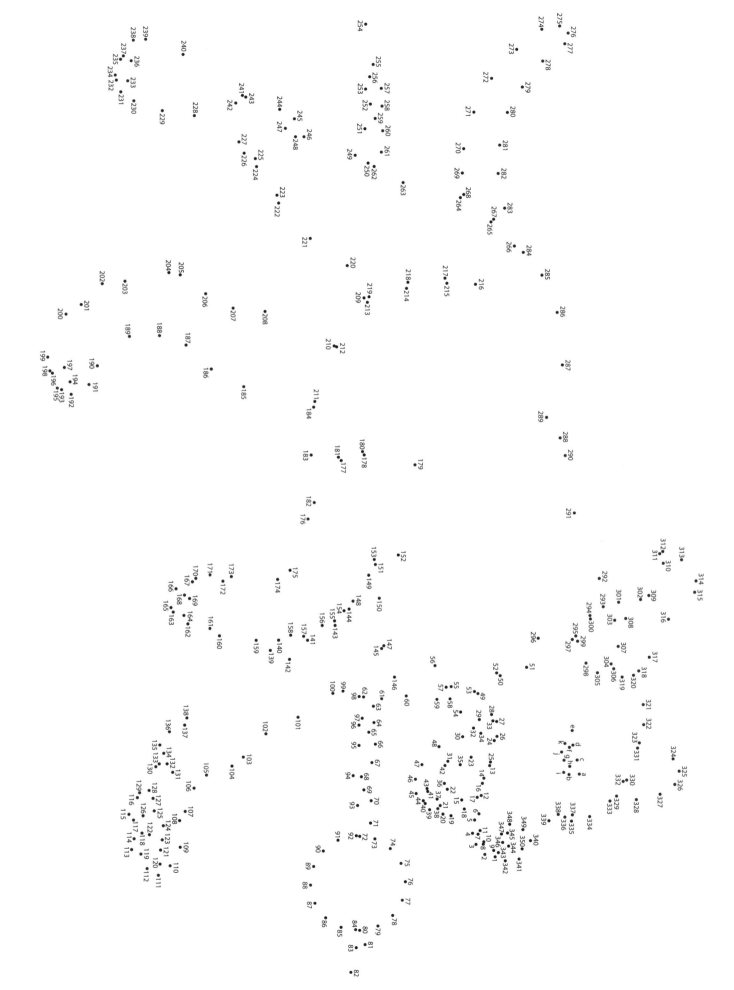

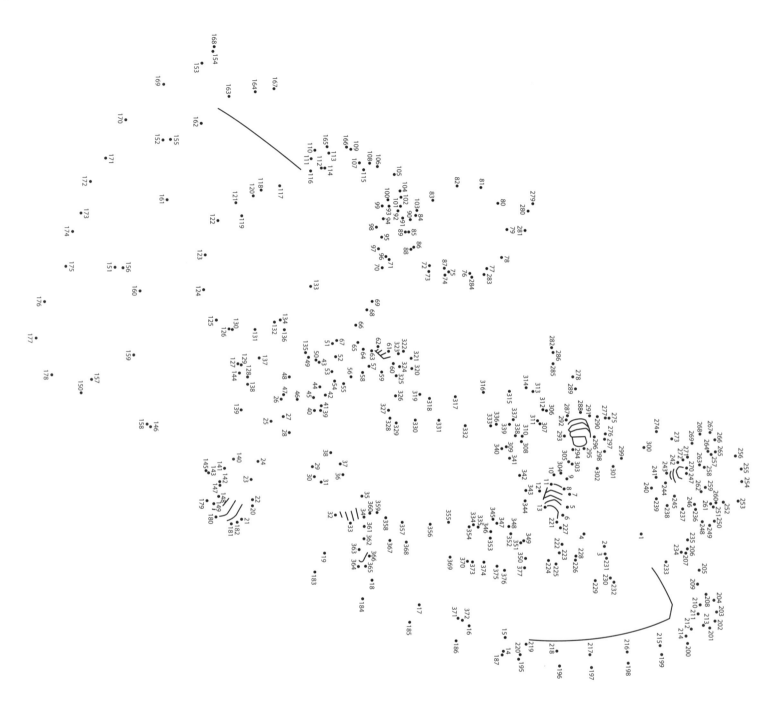

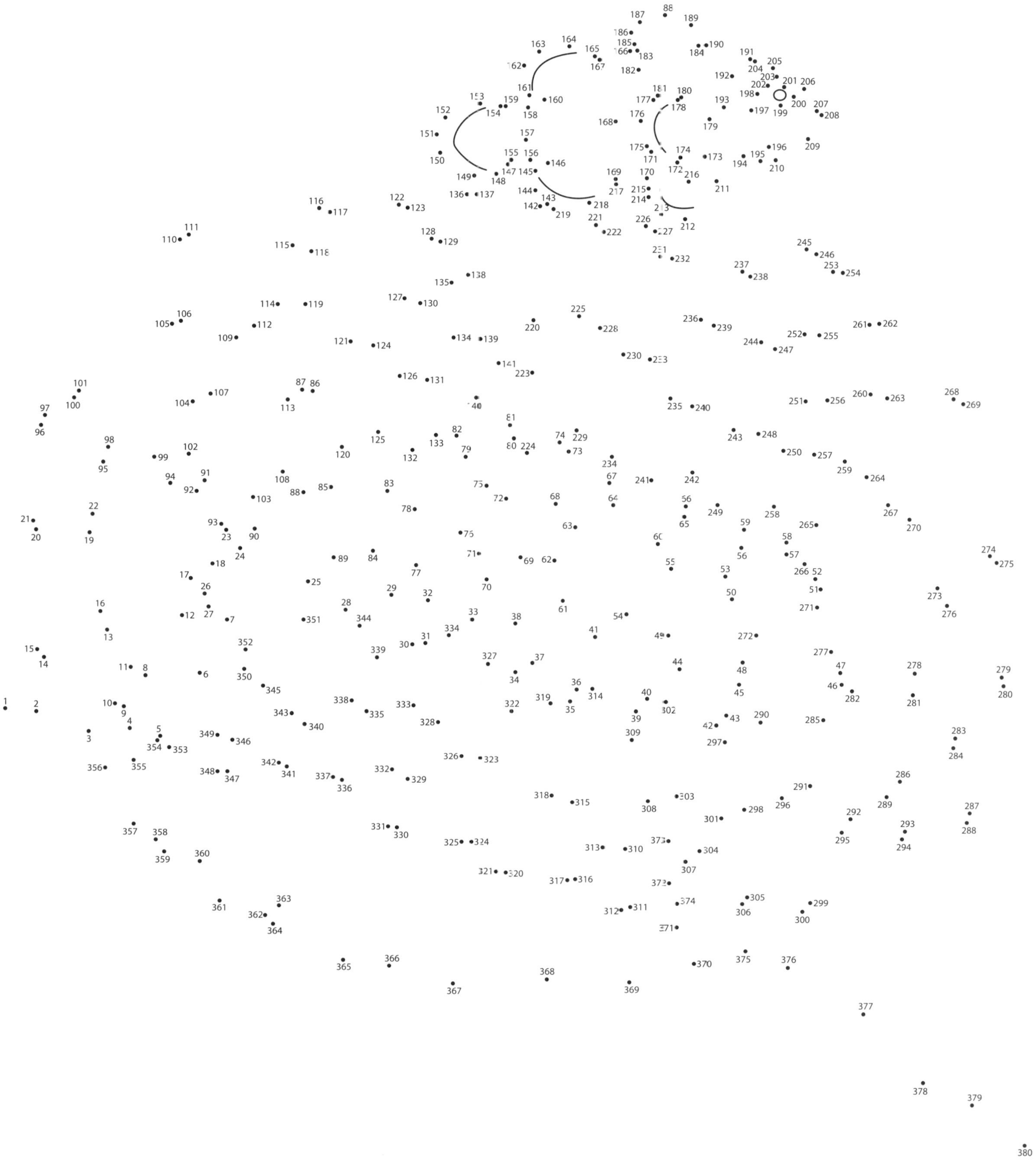

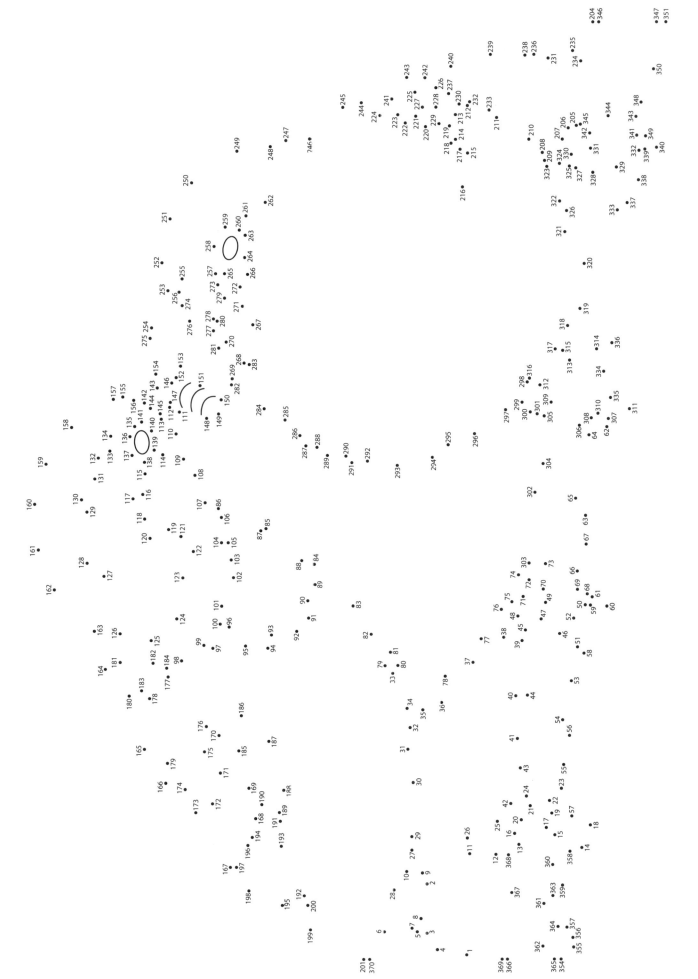

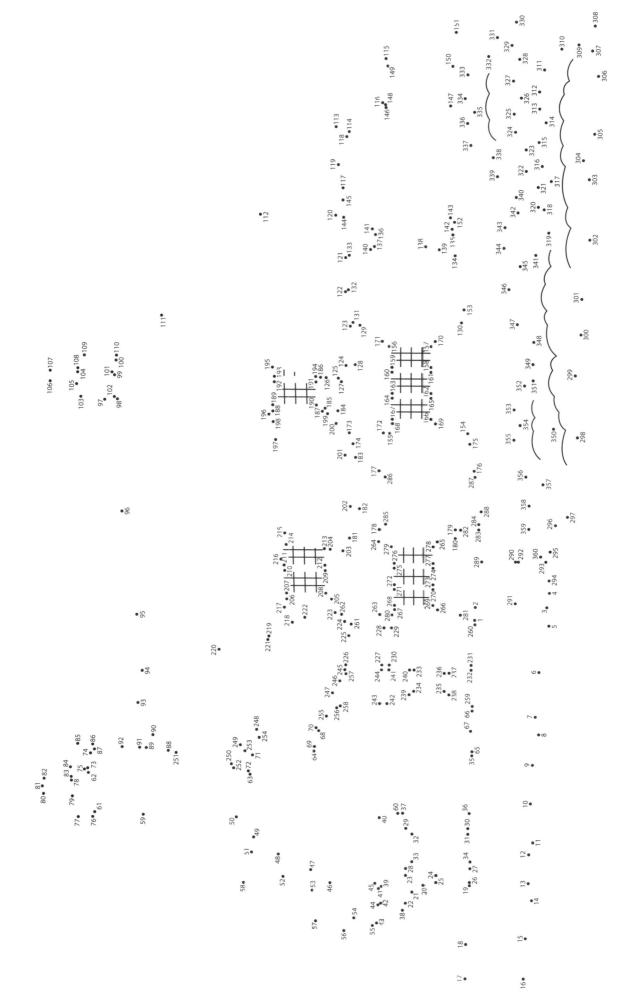

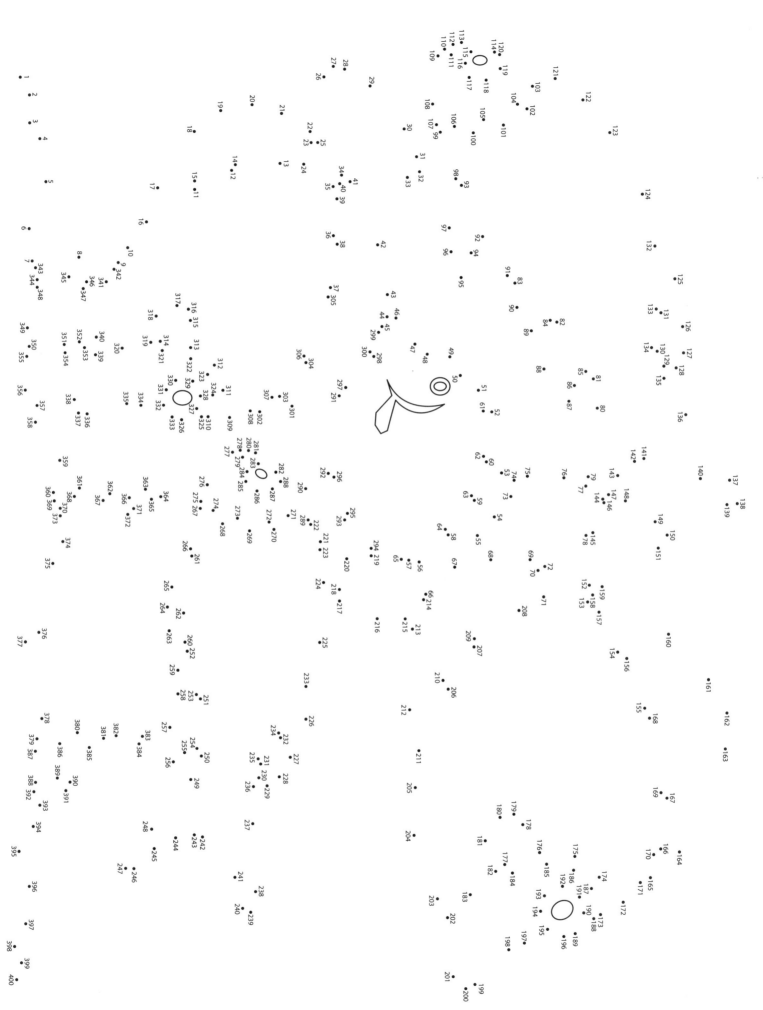

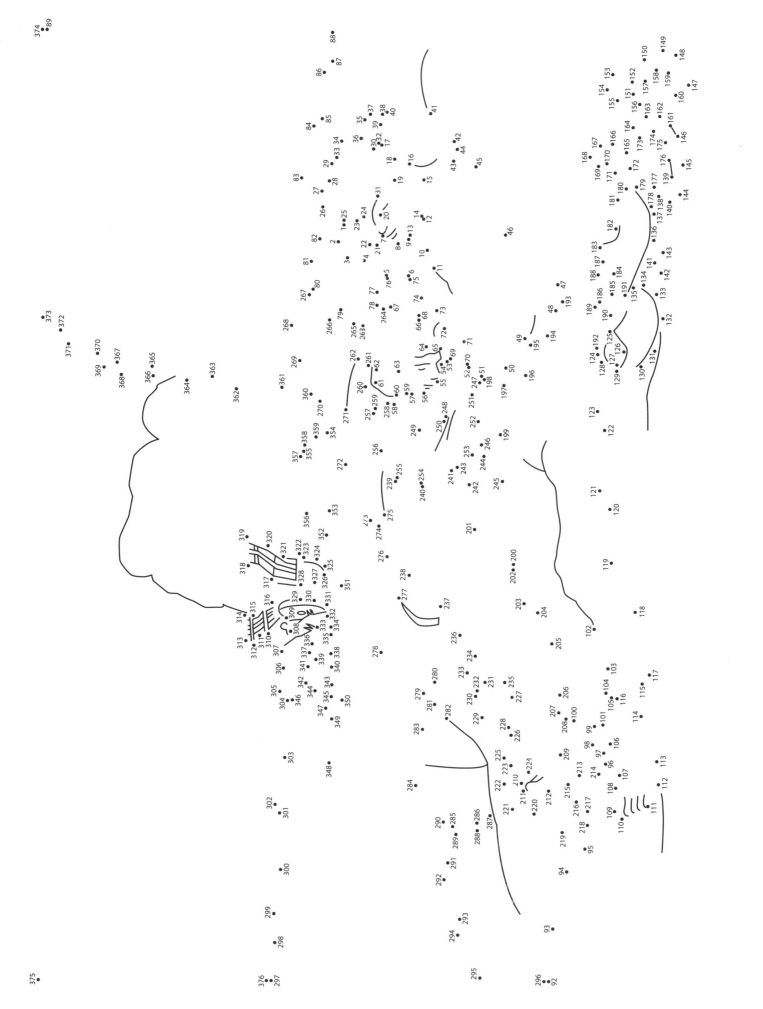

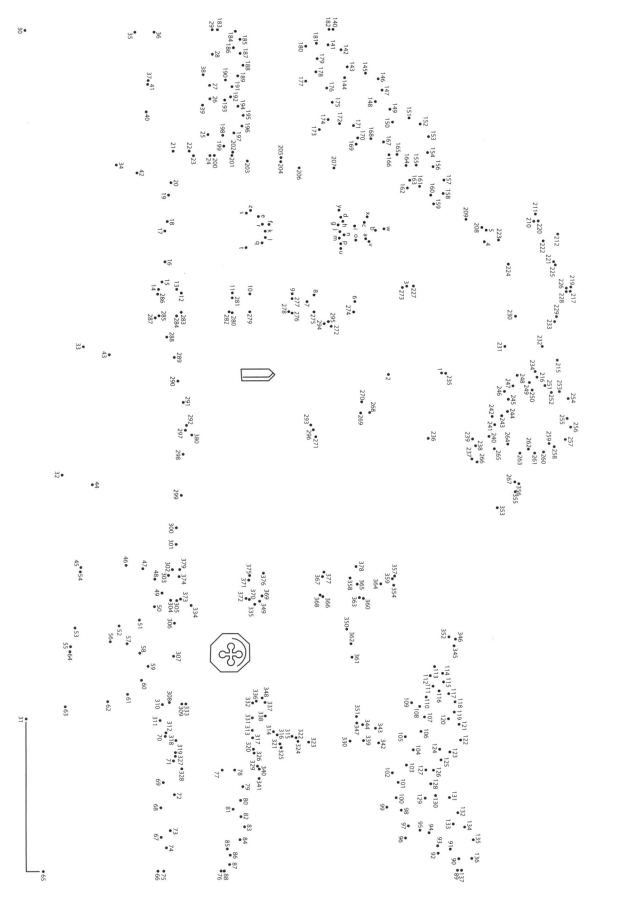

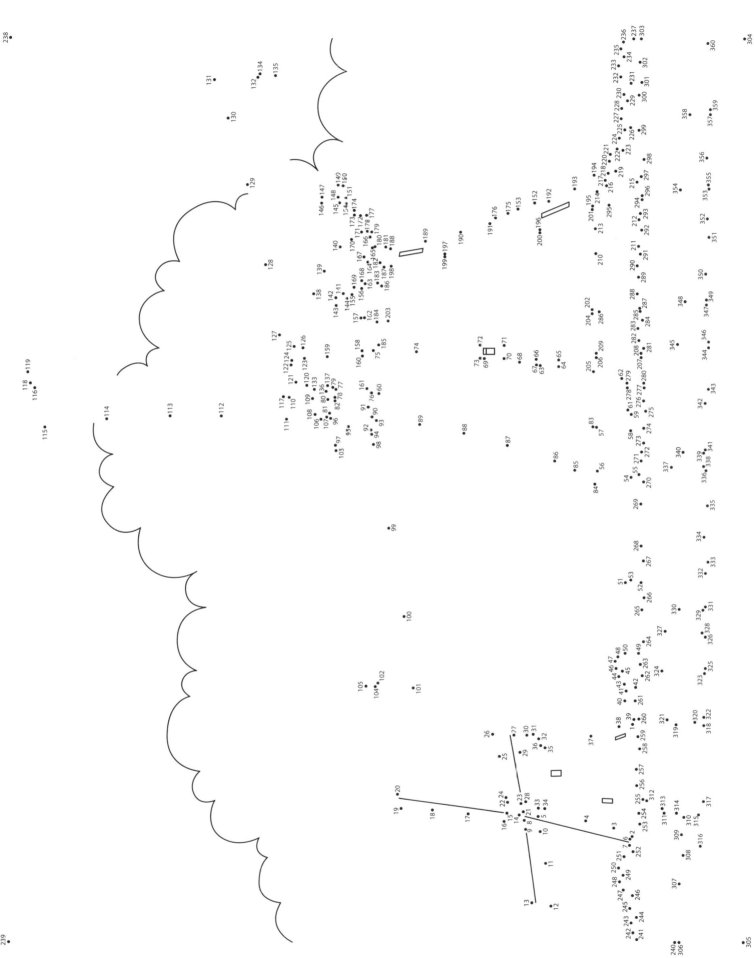

125

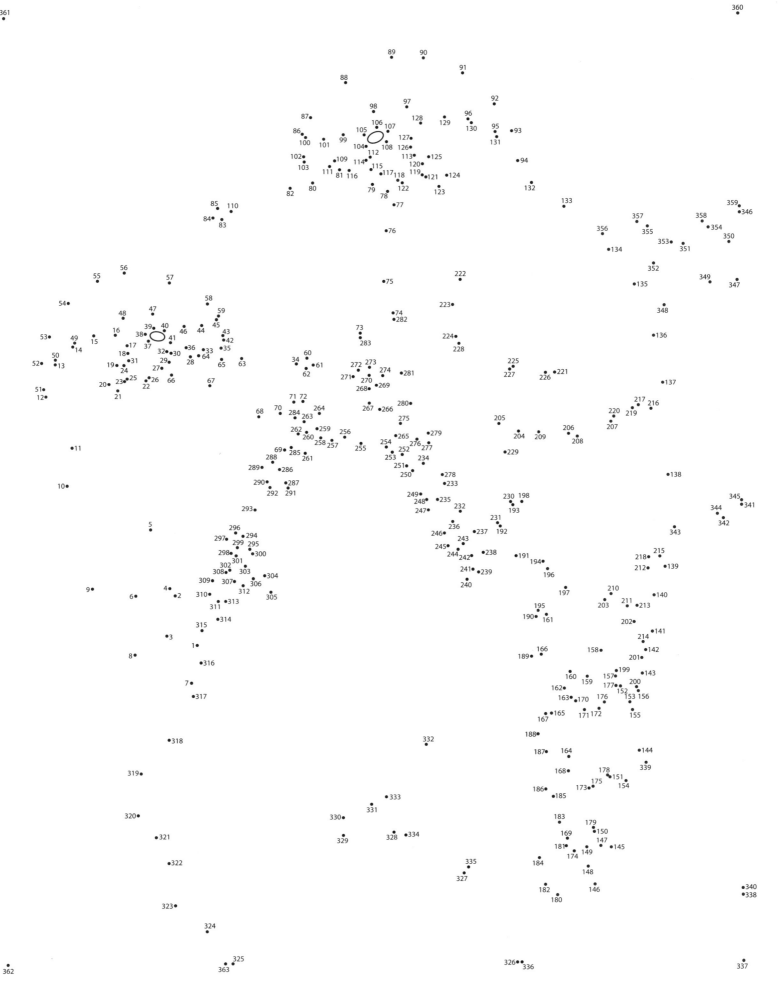

List of Illustrations